The
Logic Problems
Collection

This edition published by Parragon in 2008

Parragon
Queen Street House
4 Queen Street
Bath BA1 1HE, UK

ISBN: 978-1-4075-4419-9

A copy of the British Cataloguing-in-Publication Data is available from the British Library.

Printed in Indonesia.

The
Logic Problems
Collection

Bath · New York · Singapore · Hong Kong · Cologne · Delhi · Melbourne

Puzzle No 1

Birthday Boy

Young Jacob was celebrating his third birthday and he received cards from three people who lived in other parts of the country. Can you match the designs on the cards with the name of the sender, her connection with Jacob and the place where she lives?

Clues

1 Jacob's grandma chose the card with the teddy-bear on it.

2 Aunt Laura isn't the person from Crewe, who sent Jacob the card depicting the cat.

3 Esme sent her card from Oxford.

	Esme	Laura	Rachel	Aunt	Godmother	Grandma	Crewe	Oxford	Tavistock
Cat									
Rabbits									
Teddy-bear									
Crewe							
Oxford							
Tavistock							
Aunt				
Godmother				
Grandma				

Design	Name	Connection	Town

Puzzle No 2

Sun Seekers

Three neighbouring families chose holidays abroad this year. Can you work out the numbers of their houses, their chosen holiday destinations and the months during which they were away?

Clues

1 The Browns, who don't live at No 8, went to Lanzarote.

2 The Smiths took their holiday in June.

3 One family went to the Algarve in July.

4 The Greens live at No 6.

	No 6	No 8	No 10	Algarve	Cyprus	Lanzarote	May	June	July
Brown									
Green									
Smith									
May									
June									
July									
Algarve									
Cyprus									
Lanzarote									

Name	House number	Destination	Month

Puzzle No 3

Circumfailures

Within twenty-four hours of the start of the Daily Lantern's single-handed round-the-world yacht race, four vessels were forced to drop out. Can you work out the name of each yacht, the name of its solitary sailor, how far it sailed before disaster struck and the cause of it failing to circumnavigate the globe?

Clues
1 The Clansman had travelled only 16 miles when disaster struck.
2 Kay Kidd's yacht, which was swamped by a freak wave, wasn't Clansman or Vesta.
3 Tom Teach's yacht got further than the boat whose rudder broke when exposed to open sea conditions.
4 Larry Lafitte's yacht had a name one letter longer than that of the vessel which sprang a leak, leaving its crewperson to be rescued by a Royal Navy helicopter.
5 Mick Morgan's yacht travelled two miles further than the Vesta.

	Kay Kidd	Larry Lafitte	Mick Morgan	Tom Teach	14 miles	16 miles	18 miles	20 miles	Hit rock	Rudder broke	Sprang leak	Swamped
Clansman												
Katinka												
Shrimp												
Vesta												
Hit rock												
Rudder broke												
Sprang leak												
Swamped												
14 miles												
16 miles												
18 miles												
20 miles												

Yacht	Sailor	Distance sailed	Disaster

Puzzle No 4

Lots of Strangeness

At a recent sale held by a famous London auction house, the first four lots offered were ethnic artefacts of great strangeness. From the given clues, can you work out the nationality and description of each lot and the price for which it was sold?

Clues

1 The crundle-fan (used, obviously, for fanning crundles) was sold immediately after the Calathumpian artefact.

2 The Mukkinese battle-horn appeared on the next line in the sale catalogue after the lot which sold for a mere £800.

3 Lot 2 was knocked down to an American collector for £600.

4 The Anjinian article sold for £100 more than lot 1 and £200 more than the nose-flute.

	Anjinian	Calathumpian	Mukkinese	Prytesmic	Battle-horn	Crundle-fan	Nose-flute	Whelk-scraper	£500	£600	£700	£800
Lot 1												
Lot 2												
Lot 3												
Lot 4												
£500												
£600												
£700												
£800												
Battle-horn												
Crundle-fan												
Nose-flute												
Whelk-scraper												

Lot	Origin	Artefact	Price

Puzzle No 5

Managing a Break

Four managers from different departments of a major manufacturing company are taking 'active holidays'. Can you work out the full name of each person, which department they're in charge of and which activity holiday they are enjoying?

Clues

1 The personnel manager and the person taking the hot-air ballooning holiday are of the same sex and neither is surnamed Lane.

2 The production manager is spending two weeks scuba-diving in the Caribbean.

3 Beth is mountaineering in the Swiss Alps.

4 The sales manager's surname is Spencer and Colin's is King. The person surnamed Robbins who's gone yachting in the Aegean isn't Dawn.

	King	Lane	Robbins	Spencer	Accounts	Personnel	Production	Sales	Ballooning	Mountaineering	Scuba-diving	Yachting
Alan												
Beth												
Colin												
Dawn												
Ballooning												
Mountaineering												
Scuba-diving												
Yachting												
Accounts												
Personnel												
Production												
Sales												

First name	Surname	Department	Holiday activity

Puzzle No 6

Step Down Here!

Five members of the audience were invited to 'Step down here' to take part in the TV quiz show *Spot The Value*. Each in turn gave an estimated value for the highly desirable consumer item displayed (one quoting the exact figure!). Can you match each contestant with the order in which he/she took part, his or her home town and the value each gave? In addition, can you work out the actual value of the item?

Forenames: Agatha; Dawn; Leonard; Martina; Richard
Home towns: Esher; Filey; Gravesend; Taunton; York
Estimates: £150; £175; £180; £200; £210

Clues
1 The contestants took up positions 1 to 5 in the diagram in the order they were invited to 'Step down here', Leonard being called immediately after the woman from Gravesend, whose estimate was £180.
2 The estimate given by the first contestant, who wasn't from Filey, was £175.
3 Martina from Esher suggested a value lower than £200, an amount proffered by a previous contestant.
4 The third contestant to be invited down was from York.
5 The exact price was given by a contestant standing next but one to the one from Taunton.
6 Dawn was the last of the five contestants to arrive in the line.

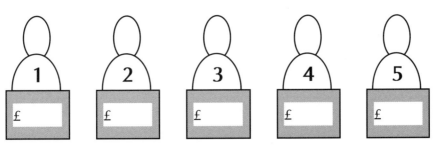

Position	Forename	Home town	Estimate

Starting tip:
First work out the order in which Leonard was asked to step down.

Puzzle No 7

Filmyflabbies

A new children's TV series is proving extremely popular, featuring five colourful characters with funny names and even funnier voices. Can you discover the name of each Filmyflabby, his or her colour, the distinctive accessory that helps identify each and the different shape each has on their tummy?

Clues

1 Dum travels about on a skateboard, but Potti isn't the purple Filmyflabby with the shopping-bag.

2 Loco's special shape isn't a star, nor does that shape belong to the Filmyflabby who carries the umbrella.

3 The pink Filmyflabby isn't identified by a triangle or star and also doesn't carry the umbrella.

4 KooKoo is blue and doesn't carry the umbrella or ride on the pogo-stick.

5 The Filmyflabby with the diamond shape wears large wellies. The yellow one has a circle shape.

6 GaGa is identified by a square shape on his tummy.

	Blue	Green	Pink	Purple	Yellow	Pogo-stick	Shopping-bag	Skateboard	Umbrella	Wellies	Circle	Diamond	Square	Star	Triangle
Dum															
GaGa															
KooKoo															
Loco															
Potti															
Circle															
Diamond															
Square															
Star															
Triangle															
Pogo-stick															
Shopping-bag															
Skateboard															
Umbrella															
Wellies															

Name	Colour	Accessory	Shape

Puzzle No 8

Late Starters

Things were going badly awry on the building site as, on successive days, five different men were late for work, each giving a different reason to the foreman. Can you match each man with his trade, say on which day he was late and identify the excuse he offered?

Clues

1 A transport problem was given as Trevor's reason for being late on Thursday.

2 The man whose wife was ill had to explain his late arrival the day before the plumber, whose excuse wasn't that he had run out of petrol.

3 It was on Wednesday that the electrician failed to turn up on time.

4 The bricklayer had to apologise to the foreman for his late arrival earlier in the week than Karl.

5 The joiner whose car wouldn't start was late for work two days earlier than Winston.

6 The man who admitted he had overslept was late on Tuesday morning; this wasn't Leslie, who isn't the plasterer.

	Bricklayer	Electrician	Joiner	Plasterer	Plumber	Monday	Tuesday	Wednesday	Thursday	Friday	Car wouldn't start	Missed bus	Overslept	Ran out of petrol	Wife ill
Karl															
Leslie															
Ryan															
Trevor															
Winston															
Car wouldn't start															
Missed bus															
Overslept															
Ran out of petrol															
Wife ill															
Monday															
Tuesday															
Wednesday															
Thursday															
Friday															

Name	Trade	Day	Excuse

Puzzle No 9

Spy Stories

Five British secret agents are being infiltrated into the South American republic of San Guinari to keep an eye on the local activities of the international criminal organisation IKON. Can you work out the real name and service number of each agent and the name and occupation given on the passport he or she is using to enter San Guinari?

Clues

1 The person pretending to be Sandy Tyler (is Sandy short for Alexander or Sandra?) isn't Agent K20 from the K (surveillance) section.

2 Dorothy Elton's section identification letter is earlier in the alphabet than that of the agent posing as an engineer, who isn't X15.

3 X27, the agent of the X (action) section, whose cover is as a travel writer for the *Sunday Messenger*, isn't Andrew Brooke.

4 Jane Kavanagh is travelling on a fake passport bearing the name Kelly Locke.

5 Mark Newcombe, whose documents describe him as a salesman for the multinational Penny Corporation's military equipment division, isn't travelling on Jean Kervin's Canadian passport.

6 G34, the radio operator from the G (communications) section, is posing as Chris Dixon.

7 Gerald Howard, known officially as agent K12, isn't the infiltrator pretending to be Pat Quinlan, a naturalist interested in San Guinari's flora and fauna.

	G34	K12	K20	X15	X27	Chris Dixon	Jean Kervin	Kelly Locke	Pat Quinlan	Sandy Tyler	Engineer	Journalist	Naturalist	Salesman	Tourist
Andrew Brooke															
Dorothy Elton															
Gerald Howard															
Jane Kavanagh															
Mark Newcombe															
Engineer															
Journalist															
Naturalist															
Salesman															
Tourist															
Chris Dixon															
Jean Kervin															
Kelly Locke															
Pat Quinlan															
Sandy Tyler															

Real name	Service number	False name	False occupation

Puzzle No 10

Stone Age Sport

Stone Age heroes Agg, Egg, Igg, Ogg and Ugg once got their heads together and decided to invent a sport called wrestling. Each competed at a different weight. Can you match them with their opponents on the first bill they staged, say at which weight each contest was fought and work out the order in which the bouts were staged in the large cavern which served as the arena for the event?

Clues

1 The first bout was the hog-weight contest, which didn't involve Jugg.

2 Igg was the sabre-tooth-tiger-weight wrestler.

3 Hugg, the mouse-weight opponent, sought to achieve success by encircling his opponent's body with his thin, but muscular, arms.

4 Thugg, who was just plain vicious, was a participant in the fourth bout of the session; his opponent wasn't Ogg.

5 Agg's contest was the third on the bill.

6 The bout between Egg and Slugg, the latter's style involving standing and flailing his arms like a windmill (which had, of course, not yet been invented), was the next one after the mammoth-weight contest.

	Hugg	Jugg	Lugg	Slugg	Thugg	Mouse-weight	Jackal-weight	Hog-weight	Sabre-tooth-tiger-weight	Mammoth-weight	First	Second	Third	Fourth	Fifth
Agg															
Egg															
Igg															
Ogg															
Ugg															
First															
Second															
Third															
Fourth															
Fifth															
Mouse-weight															
Jackal-weight															
Hog-weight															
S'-tooth-tiger-weight															
Mammoth-weight															

Hero	Opponent	Weight	Order

Puzzle No 11

In the Picture

The walls of the foyer at a West End theatre are adorned with photographs of actors and actresses who have appeared there in the past. Can you fully identify the thespian depicted in each of the photos lettered A to H in the diagram?

Forenames: Dee; Edgar; Grant; Lavinia; Marshall; Nancy; Patricia; Roger
Surnames: Claim; Gallery; Hammett; Lynes; Pitt; Prompt; Queue; Stage

Clues

1 Dee Claim's photo has that of the performer named Hammett to its left and Roger's to its right.
2 The portrait of Queue, who isn't Edgar, hangs directly opposite on the left of the foyer to that of Patricia on the right.
3 Lavinia's photo is somewhere to the left of Pitt's on the same wall.
4 Grant is the subject of portrait F.
5 The first name of the thespian portrayed in photograph H doesn't have five letters.
6 Lynes's photo is two places to the left of Marshall's.
7 Gallery's portrait hangs in position C, but Stage's isn't in position G.

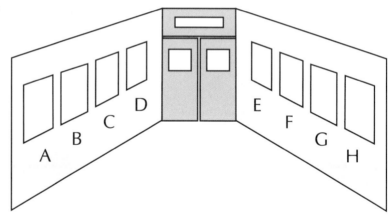

Photo	Forename	Surname

Photo	Forename	Surname

Starting tip:

First work out the position of Roger's photograph.

Puzzle No 12

To Market, to Market…

Five farmers have driven their animals to market to sell them and to buy provisions and equipment. From the following verse, can you work out how many of which type of animal each farmer was selling and what he bought?

Clues

Higgins took his pigs to market,
Another took one cow;
McTavish wasn't selling goats,
But bought himself a plough.

He who took the goats to sell
(Of which there weren't four)
Didn't buy the sack of meal,
Nor did he buy the straw.

'Twas he who had two beasts to sell
(Not sheep) who bought the straw;
Webster brought just one or two,
The one with three was Moore.

One had five to sell (not ducks)
He didn't buy the gun;
He with ducks went home with grain
When market-day was done.

	1	2	3	4	5	Cow	Ducks	Goats	Pigs	Sheep	Grain	Gun	Meal	Plough	Straw
Higgins															
Hodgson															
McTavish															
Moore															
Webster															
Grain											
Gun											
Meal											
Plough											
Straw											
Cow											
Ducks											
Goats											
Pigs											
Sheep											

Farmer	No of animals	Type of animal	Item purchased

Safety Factor

Five holidaymakers staying in a Mediterranean resort were well aware of the dangers of over-exposure to the sun. Each had brought a different brand of sun-tan preparation with a different sun-protection factor. Can you match the five with the brand they had chosen, its protection factor and its price?

Clues

1 The brand with the sun-protection factor of 15 was the most expensive.

2 Yvonne, who used the factor 2 preparation, didn't pay an exact number of pounds for it.

3 Safe-Sun wasn't the brand with the factor 6 rating.

4 Bronzetone was the product with the factor of 4.

5 The bottle of Taneezee cost its user £4.75; its factor was the next one lower than that of the £7.00 brand.

6 The product which cost £6.50 had a protection factor two higher than Edward's preparation and two lower than Michelle's, which wasn't Safe-Sun.

7 Oliver's chosen brand was Supersol.

	Bronzetone	Safe-Sun	Supersol	Taneezee	Tropique	Factor 2	Factor 4	Factor 6	Factor 8	Factor 15	£4.75	£5.00	£6.50	£7.00	£8.50
Chloe															
Edward															
Michelle															
Oliver															
Yvonne															
£4.75															
£5.00															
£6.50															
£7.00															
£8.50															
Factor 2															
Factor 4															
Factor 6															
Factor 8															
Factor 15															

Name	Brand	Factor	Price

Puzzle No 14

Sam's Samples

Laura's pet Labrador, Sam, has a habit of chewing everything which comes through the letterbox if his mistress isn't around. On five occasions last year he managed to leave the contents of five separate free samples of different products scattered all over the doormat. Can you establish all the details?

Clues

1 It was on a single digit date that Laura discovered her doormat besmeared with McCavitys' toothpaste in an exciting new flavour.

2 On one date in May (not the 15th) Laura came home to find Sam foaming at the mouth. She realised that the cause wasn't rabies, but the soap powder sample.

3 Wicks' product was tested out by Sam on the 8th day of the month.

4 Bryants weren't the manufacturers of the free sample of shampoo.

5 The brand new product from Ogdens had the benefit of Sam's attentions in July.

6 Sam's last misadventure of the year took place on the 25th of November.

7 The sample of talcum powder from the cosmetics firm was targeted by Sam on the 4th of a later month than the one when the Pollards product was savaged.

	4th	7th	8th	15th	25th	Coffee	Cosmetics	Shampoo	Soap powder	Toothpaste	Bryants	McCavitys	Ogdens	Pollards	Wicks
March															
May															
July															
September															
November															
Bryants															
McCavitys															
Ogdens															
Pollards															
Wicks															
Coffee															
Cosmetics															
Shampoo															
Soap powder															
Toothpaste															

Month	Day	Product	Company

Puzzle No 15

Where There is Discord...

The fan club of the pop group The Discords was run by five women who each had a different role on the committee. Can you fully identify the five, name her committee role and say which of the five members of the group is her particular favourite?

Clues

1 None of the women has an identical initial for her first name and surname and no first name or surname initial matches the initial of the member of The Discords any of the women prefers.

2 Janet is the secretary of the Discords' Fan Club, while the treasurer isn't Miss Jarring.

3 Dirk isn't the Discord whose greatest fan is Miss Jangle.

4 The Fan Club chairperson's surname is Harsh, but her first name isn't Selma.

5 Ryan is Christine's favourite Discord.

6 Melanie Tone-Deff isn't the Fan Club's membership secretary, whose favourite Discord is Stefan.

7 Miss Rawcuss has a signed photograph of her favourite, Bongo.

	Harsh	Jangle	Jarring	Rawcuss	Tone-Deff	Chairperson	Membership sec	Press Officer	Secretary	Treasurer	Bongo	Dirk	Jake	Ryan	Stefan
Christine															
Janet															
Melanie															
Selma															
Trudy															
Bongo															
Dirk															
Jake															
Ryan															
Stefan															
Chairperson															
Membership sec															
Press officer															
Secretary															
Treasurer															

First name	Surname	Office	Favourite

Puzzle No 16

Summer Jigsaw

Each of the boxes in the diagram contains a word which either precedes or follows the word SUMMER in a commonly-used phrase. Can you place each word in its correct box?

Words: FETE; HOLIDAY; HOUSE; INDIAN; LAST; MID; SCHOOL; SOLSTICE; TERM; TIME; WEIGHT; WINE

Clues

1 LAST is the word in the box immediately below WEIGHT and immediately left of HOUSE.
2 The word in box 11 is made up of an even number of letters.
3 TERM appropriately appears in the same vertical column as SCHOOL, which is somewhere above it.
4 FETE appears in an odd-numbered box immediately to the right of WINE.
5 Box 7 is the one which contains the word SOLSTICE.
6 The word in box 5 is the same length as the one in box 9.
7 TIME is separated horizontally from INDIAN only by the word HOLIDAY.
8 The word in box 2 is longer than the one in box 8.

1	2	3	4
5	6	7	8
9	10	11	12

Starting tip:

The LAST shall be (placed) first!

- 17 -

Puzzle No 17

Freshers' Fancy

A group of undergraduates were reminiscing about the first week of their University careers the previous autumn. Each had attended the Freshers' Evening, when all the clubs and societies ran stalls and invited newcomers to join. Can you identify the club each had signed up for, on which night of the week it had held its first meeting and how many members were present?

Clues

1 It transpired that the wine-tasting society had attracted the highest turn-out; its first meeting was two days after that of the astronomy society, which wasn't attended by 21 students.

2 The first meeting of the French film club, attended by Emma, attracted more students than the sailing club, but fewer than attended the Tuesday meeting.

3 There were more members at the Monday meeting than at that of the society Kate joined, which met on a Wednesday.

4 David was one of just ten members present at the initial meeting of the club he had joined, which took place two days after the inaugural meeting of the play-reading group.

5 John's meeting took place earlier in the week than Ian's.

	Astronomy	French films	Play-reading	Sailing	Wine-tasting	Monday	Tuesday	Wednesday	Thursday	Friday	6	10	15	21	30
David															
Emma															
Ian															
John															
Kate															
6															
10															
15															
21															
30															
Monday															
Tuesday															
Wednesday															
Thursday															
Friday															

Name	Group	Day	Number

Puzzle No 18

Arms and the Man

The Grand-Duke Hans Niess-und-Bumpzer-Dazi had a very long pedigree, giving rise to the four quarterings on his coat-of-arms. Can you name the creature depicted in each of the quarters numbered 1 to 4, say in which colour it is displayed and name the Middle-European family whose arms were introduced into the Grand-Duke's family as a result of various dynastic marriages over the centuries?

Creatures: Dragon; eagle; elephant; lion
Colours: Black; blue; orange; pink
Families: Klotzky; Muddelkopf; Nitwitz; von Plonka

Clues

1 The pink elephant, badge of a family of noted drinkers, appears in the quarter directly above the one inherited from the Klotzky family arms.

2 The creature which is depicted in black has appeared on the Grand-Ducal arms since Hans' grandfather married the eldest daughter of Count von Plonka.

3 The lion of the Muddelkopfs, which isn't orange, is to be seen in an odd-numbered quarter of the arms.

4 The dragon is immediately to the right of the blue creature.

Quarter	Creature	Colour	Family

Starting tip:

Begin by identifying the creature depicted in quarter number 4.

Puzzle No 19

Waking Moments

Yesterday evening five businessmen staying overnight in an hotel phoned the reception area to request alarm calls this morning; they also each made a second request. Can you work out who is in every room (rooms on the first floor begin with '1', those on the 2nd with '2', etc), the time of the alarm call and the other request made of the receptionist?

Clues

1 Mr Harvey requested a 6.45 alarm call, while Mr Price ordered a late supper in his room.

2 Mr Henderson (who isn't in room 104) wanted to be woken earlier than Mr Price.

3 The occupant of room 112 neither requested the 6.30 alarm call nor asked for a taxi to be ordered; the guest who requested the earliest call and that his suit be pressed in time for the morning wasn't on the first floor.

4 The occupant of room 208 asked to be woken half an hour later than the one who wanted to have breakfast in his room.

5 The 7.15 wake-up call was put through to room 401.

6 Mr Bryant's room number is 316.

	Room 104	Room 112	Room 208	Room 316	Room 401	6.15	6.30	6.45	7.00	7.15	Breakfast in room	Check train times	Late supper in room	Order taxi	Press suit
Bryant															
Harvey															
Henderson															
Price															
Spencer															
B'fast in room															
Check train times															
Late supper															
Order taxi															
Press suit															
6.15															
6.30															
6.45															
7.00															
7.15															

Guest	Room number	Alarm call	Other request

Tor Tour

The famous Five Tors Moorland Cross-country Run takes place each year. From the following details, can you discover the order in which entrants have to visit the tors, the direction from which each tor is approached and their heights?

Clues

1 Pavey Tor (which isn't 1,130 feet high) isn't the first to be reached. Neither Pavey nor the 1,130-foot one is fifth.

2 The tor approached from the south-east is higher than the last one, but it isn't the highest, which is the third to be visited.

3 The fifth tor isn't Camworthy Tor, which is approached from the north-east.

4 Runners approach the fourth tor from the south-west and the 940-foot peak from the north-west.

5 The 1,560-foot tor is neither Chagley Tor nor Binaton Tor, which is visited second.

6 Highpound Tor is a mere 890 feet above sea level and runners don't approach it from the east.

	East	North-east	North-west	South-east	South-west	Binaton Tor	Camworthy Tor	Chagley Tor	Highpound Tor	Pavey Tor	890 feet	940 feet	1,130 feet	1,560 feet	1,840 feet
First															
Second															
Third															
Fourth															
Fifth															
890 feet															
940 feet															
1,130 feet															
1,560 feet															
1,840 feet															
Binaton Tor															
Camworthy Tor															
Chagley Tor															
Highpound Tor															
Pavey Tor															

Order	Direction	Name of tor	Height

Puzzle No 21

You Have Been Selected ...

On five consecutive days last week, a congratulatory message came through Jo's letter box, stating that it was almost definite that she'd win a considerable sum if she ordered at least one item from the accompanying catalogue. Can you work out which type of items Jo was offered every day, which bucolically-named woman signed each letter and how much was being offered as a prize?

Clues

1 The letter from the health products firm came the day before the one signed by Lavinia Glenn, which promised a higher reward.

2 The letter accompanying the gardening catalogue held out the prospect of enriching Jo with over £1,000 more than Tuesday's offer, but not as much as that (not the first to arrive) to which Alison Meadows had appended her signature.

3 The brochure containing details of bargains in household goods reached Jo the day after she'd reached the final stages of the draw for £12,000.

4 The opportunity to purchase books came later than both the letter from Caroline Dale and the one offering £10,000 (which arrived the day before Ms Dale's).

5 The £9,000 bait arrived the day after the clothing catalogue but more than a day before Melanie Vaill's letter.

6 The sum promised by Katy Campion was over £1,000 more than the one disclosed in the Friday literature.

Day	Goods offered	Signatory	Prize

Puzzle No 22

Dynasty

The pupils of Class 4 of a junior school were recently given the task of inventing a country and describing its institutions. In one such country, the monarch had died without an heir and a new dynasty had been established. Can you insert the names of the founder and his wife, together with those of his four sons and (below these) the names of their wives in the family tree?

Men's names: Binko; Bonko; Cranko; Plonko; Grunko
Women's names: Blinka; Bunka; Clinka; Flunka; Twinka

Clues
1 Cranko is next in age above Twinka's husband, but he is younger than Clinka's husband, who is neither Binko nor the son born next before Binko.

2 Flunka's husband is next lower in the line of succession after Plonko.

3 If the new ruler died, Bonko would have precedence over Blinka's husband.

4 The fourth son's name doesn't have the same internal vowel as his wife's, unlike that of the founder of the dynasty.

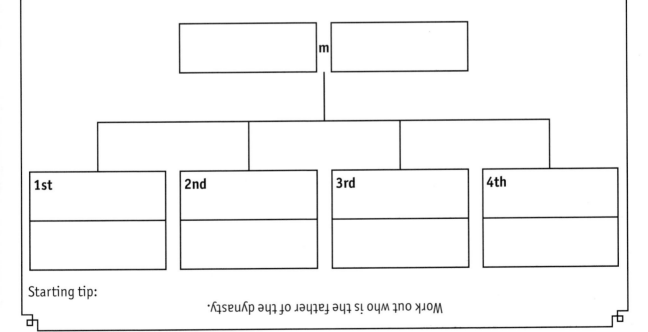

Starting tip:

Work out who is the father of the dynasty.

Puzzle No 23

Robotixcops

Robotixcops, the galaxy's biggest producer of mechanical workers in the 24th Century, build a number of special law-enforcement models and a selection are about to be shipped to police forces on different parts of the planet Terra, formerly known as Earth. Can you work out the name and number of each unit, its specialised role and which city's police force it's destined to join?

Clues

1 The 'Howard's' number, which like that of all male-named robots ends in an odd digit, is lower than that of the 'Daphne'; the 'Thelma' isn't being purchased by the metropolitan Police Force of Southbrit, the megacity stretching from the English Channel to the Midlands.

2 One of the male robots, though not model 2317, is programmed as a speed cop and another is on its way to Adelbourne, the Australian city created when buildings from Melbourne and Adelaide met.

3 The 'Howard', which is on its way to Sahara City in North Africa, isn't the Robotixcops product designated as a specialist administrator. The crossing patrol robot is female while the other female robot will be joining the New York Police Department.

4 The 'Martin', which isn't model 2317, isn't the male robot that is being sent to Ulan Bator; the beat cop has a higher first digit in its model number than the 'Martin'.

Robot name	Model number	Speciality	Destination

- 24 -

Puzzle No 24

Tasting the Tipple

In this week's wine magazine, five experts are asked to choose their best value supermarket wine. Can you discover which wine each chose, the variety and which supermarket sold it?

Clues

1 Max Tipler chose St Michel, which isn't a Chablis. Phil Glass also doesn't favour the Chablis.

2 Neither Max Tipler nor Ivor Cork recommends a wine from Asco.

3 Chateau Dufay is a Burgundy. It isn't Phil Glass's choice nor the wine chosen by Phil's colleague, which is now available from Asco.

4 Baron Claude is sold by Waitway supermarkets. Max Tipler's choice isn't sold at Co-fields stores.

5 Neuchamps is sold by Tesrose, but isn't a Beaujolais or a Cabernet Sauvignon.

6 Lena Barr goes for the Cabernet Sauvignon, which isn't the wine bottled by Abbe Phillipe.

	Beaujolais	Burgundy	Cabernet Sauvignon	Chablis	Entre-Deux-Mers	Ivor Cork	Jilly Van Blonck	Lena Barr	Max Tipler	Phil Glass	Asco	Co-fields	Gatebury	Tesrose	Waitway
Abbe Phillipe															
Baron Claude															
Chateau Dufay															
Neuchamps															
St Michel															
Asco															
Co-fields															
Gatebury															
Tesrose															
Waitway															
Ivor Cork															
Jilly Van Blonck															
Lena Barr															
Max Tipler															
Phil Glass															

Name	Variety	Expert	Store

Puzzle No 25

Off the Rails

The Great London and Provincial Railway Company introduced their Ship class locomotives in the summer of 1923 – and withdrew them just a week later after five had been involved in spectacular accidents caused by mechanical failures but, luckily, without any serious casualties. Can you work out the name of the locomotive which crashed each day, what happened and what failure caused the accident?

Clues

1 The Waratah, named after a ship which vanished off the African coast, was involved in the Friday incident; the Hesperus didn't crash on Tuesday.

2 On Thursday, a connecting-rod in the running gear of one of the Ship class engines fractured.

3 The explosion which destroyed Bangsby Station when the boiler of a locomotive burst occurred the day before the Mary Celeste's accident.

4 The accident caused by a regulator jamming happened earlier in the week than the failure of the valve gear, which didn't cause one engine to run off a bridge and into a river.

5 On Monday, one of the brand-new locomotives left the rails, ran down an embankment and overturned on a road.

6 The locomotive Titanic was destroyed in a collision, though not with an iceberg.

7 The brakes failed on the Lusitania.

Day	Locomotive	Accident	Cause

Puzzle No 26

Cactus Creek

In the year 1884, the town of Cactus Creek, Arizona – in the heart of the Wild West – boasted one hundred and twenty citizens, one general store, one blacksmith's shop, no church and four saloons, though to be fair, most of the saloons' customers were cowboys from nearby ranches. Can you fill in on the plan the name of each saloon, its owner and its unique attraction?

Saloons: Gold Nugget; Lone Star; Thunderbird; Wagon Wheel
Owners: Frenchie Leroy; Joe Doolan; Miss Nelly Rogers; Tom Bowden
Attractions: Lowest prices; poker; roulette; stage show

Clues

1 The Gold Nugget Saloon was directly opposite the saloon whose main attraction was a stage show featuring a sentimental ballad singer, a pair of knockabout comics and a troupe of dancing girls.

2 Frenchie Leroy's saloon, which wasn't the Wagon Wheel and isn't marked D on the plan, was the only one in town with a roulette wheel.

3 Saloon C was the choice of cowboys who wanted to enjoy a good, if not honest, game of poker.

4 Miss Nelly Rogers owned saloon A.

5 The Lone Star Saloon, which offered drinks at the lowest prices in town, was on the same side of Cactus Creek's Main Street as Joe Doolan's establishment.

 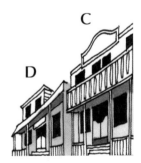

Saloon	Name	Owner	Attraction

Starting tip:

Position Frenchie Leroy's saloon

True Stories

This week's copy of *Coffee Break* magazine contains the usual crop of readers' 'true stories' under sensational headlines. Can you work out which page each story appears on, the headline and the names of the central women and men involved?

Clues

1 'I married my brother-in-law' shouts the headline on page 5, but Greg isn't the man involved. Martin features in the story on page 8.

2 Karen tells all on page 14, while 'I can't forget him' is found three pages after Annie's dramatic revelations.

3 'I can't stop cheating' appears six pages before the story involving Jon.

4 Phil is the erring spouse in the 'She stole my husband' story.

5 'He won't talk to me' wails Beverley.

6 Jean's story in *Coffee Break* tells us all the details about Bob.

Page	Headline	Woman writer	Man involved

Puzzle No 28

Love's Luvvies

Harry Love (Entertainment Agency) Ltd has provided five artistes to perform in different summer show venues in the seaside resort of Brightbourne. Can you work out the full name of each of Love's five clients, what they do and where in Brightbourne they're doing it?

Clues

1 Pam's surname – professionally speaking – is McLaverty; Alma isn't Miss Pegram.

2 Fiona, who isn't employed at Manfred's Club, isn't the juggler who performs with balls, wine bottles and even razor-sharp knives.

3 Marion is performing at the Marine Theatre; Pam isn't working at the Pavilion Theatre.

4 Alma is an impressionist, working at a club entertaining audiences with her hilarious take-offs of the rich and famous; Miss Stevens, who is working at the other club, isn't a juggler.

5 Miss Wescott assists magician The Great Comus (also one of Harry's clients) who isn't featured at the Pavilion Theatre.

6 The country singer, who sports a Tennessee accent even though she is from the East End of London, is working at the Grand Theatre.

First name	Surname	Act	Venue

Puzzle No 29

In the Area

When the Storbury Show was held, six areas around the central show area, marked A to F on the plan, were each given over to different activities presided over by a member of the show committee. Can you name the attraction in each area and fully identify the person in charge?

Clues

1 The tea tent in position C in the diagram isn't under the aegis of Janet Foster.

2 Jackson is the surname of the person organising area F.

3 As you look at the plan, Ronnie, who isn't in area F, is looking after the darts competition in the area immediately right of that controlled by Sheila.

4 The football competition is taking place in the area indicated by a letter which immediately follows the one denoting the fortune-teller's tent.

5 The welly-throwing contest is taking place under the direction of Benson, in an area indicated by an odd-numbered letter in the alphabetical order, which is adjacent to the one where Pearson is on duty.

6 Lucy, whose surname isn't Walters, is looking after area D, which isn't where the children's pet show is being staged; Madge isn't in charge of the latter activity.

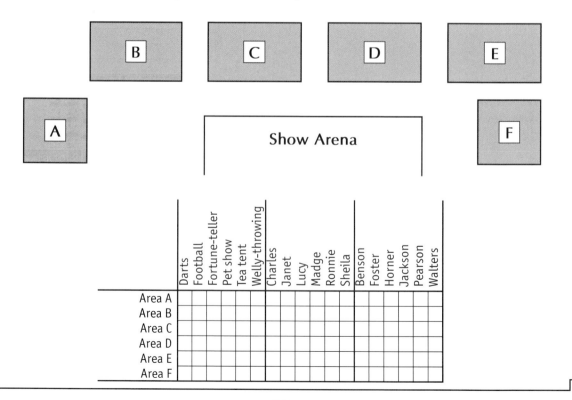

Puzzle No 30

On the Run

The final lap of the 1500 metres race was underway at the school sports day and four runners were well spaced out in the positions numbered 1 to 4 in the diagram below. Can you identify the runners and the colour of the vest each wore in the race?

Forenames: Alan; Craig; Dermot; Warren
Surnames: Hill; Lowther; Marchant; Radley
Colours: Blue; green; red; yellow

Clues
1 Dermot, being the only runner not yet to have passed the line indicating the start of the last lap, was in last place.
2 In race order, Craig was one place behind Hill, who wore the yellow vest.
3 Warren Radley wasn't the runner in blue.
4 The second-placed runner (not Lowther) wore the green vest.

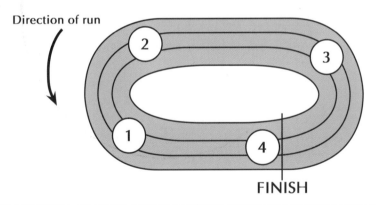

Direction of run

FINISH

Runner	Forename	Surname	Vest colour

Starting tip:

First work out Hill's position.

- 31 -

Puzzle No 31

Nicked!

Five professional villains have recently been dealt with by the courts. Can you associate the name of the arresting officers with the nickname and surname of the villain he nabbed and say for which offence each villain was charged?

Clues

1 The man arrested by DI Hunter for arson was neither Sharp nor Smart, neither of whom has the nickname Corky.

2 DI Corner nabbed Tip, who isn't Twist.

3 The man guilty of armed robbery was neither Flash nor Wiley; none of these three men was arrested by DI Catchmore.

4 DI Grabham wasn't responsible for catching either Knocker or Sharp, neither of whom was a forger; nor was the forger arrested by DI Grabham.

5 Skinner wasn't guilty of stealing, unlike both Corky and the man arrested by DI Trackman; his captive has the same number of letters in both his nickname and surname.

6 Smart, though a persistent offender, has never carried a gun.

7 The surname of Shifty doesn't begin with 'S', unlike that of the armed robber; Wiley's offence wasn't burglary.

	Nickname					Surname									
	Corky	Flash	Knocker	Shifty	Tip	Sharp	Skinner	Smart	Twist	Wiley	Armed robbery	Arson	Burglary	Car theft	Forgery
DI Catchmore															
DI Corner															
DI Grabham															
DI Hunter															
DI Trackman															
Armed robbery															
Arson															
Burglary															
Car theft															
Forgery															
Sharp															
Skinner															
Smart															
Twist															
Wiley															

Detective	Nickname	Surname	Crime

Duel Personality

Sir Rawnsley Rapier was a well-known man-about-17th-century-London, a companion of Charles II and a notorious swordsman and duellist. During a single week in 1679, he fought five duels for different trivial reasons, winning each time by wounding his opponent. Can you work out who he fought on which day, what the quarrel was about and where his opponent was wounded?

Clues

1 The duel with Sir Guy Glaive, who wasn't the man whose observation that Sir Rawnsley was putting on a little weight was taken as a gross insult, took place earlier than the fight over the game of cards.

2 The Frenchman Comte de Falchion, who received a wound in the left shoulder, fought the day after the duellist who was wounded in the right leg and the day before Sir Toby Tuck.

3 The duel over the favours of an actress, which wasn't on Friday, took place later than the one in which Sir Rawnsley wounded his opponent, who wasn't a fellow knight, in the left arm.

4 It was a fellow knight who spilled Sir Rawnsley's wine and ended up with a wound in the right arm; their duel wasn't on Monday.

5 Sir Rawnsley defeated the Hon. Hugh Hanger before taking on the man with whom he'd quarrelled about a play.

6 The duel over the play took place before the duel with Lord Claymore, whose argument didn't concern a game of cards.

	Comte de Falchion	Hon. Hugh Hanger	Lord Claymore	Sir Guy Glaive	Sir Toby Tuck	Actress	Card game	Personal insult	Play	Spilled wine	Left arm	Left shoulder	Right arm	Right leg	Right shoulder
Monday															
Tuesday															
Wednesday															
Thursday															
Friday															
Left arm															
Left shoulder															
Right arm															
Right leg															
Right shoulder															
Actress															
Card game															
Personal insult															
Play															
Spilled wine															

Day	Opponent	Quarrel origin	Wound position

Puzzle No 33

Out of Class

Five postgraduate students at the University of Goatsferry's School of Medicine are heavily involved in some of the University's spare time activity groups. Can you work out where each student comes from, what they're studying and which group they're helping to run?

Clues

1 The embryologist is a leading light of the Chess Club.

2 Marie isn't studying pathology.

3 Joan was born and bred in Bristol.

4 Graham, who is captain of the University Rugby Team, isn't the native of Lincoln who is specialising in dermatology.

5 Dan, who is studying geriatrics, isn't the postgraduate who's directing the new production of Much Ado About Nothing – the musical for the Drama Society; Dan doesn't come from Manchester.

6 The young woman from Coventry who is a mainstay of the Conservation Group isn't studying neurology.

Postgraduate	Hometown	Subject	Society

The Inn Thing

It all started when the brewery which owns The Hare and Hounds in Netherlipp decided to find a more appealing name; then four other pubs in the town followed suit. From the clues given below (and this introduction) can you work out the old and new name of each pub, its location in the town and the month in which it made the change?

Clues

1 The change to the Mermaid and Dolphin was made later than that from the Rose and Crown, but the pub in Rye Street, which isn't the former White Horse, took its name later than both.

2 No alliterative title has been changed for another alliterative one; the Hops Hill pub has neither acquired or relinquished an alliterative title. NB – An alliterative title is one in which the two main words begin with the same letter, for example: The Dog and Duck or The Yellow Yoyo.

3 The Malt Road pub, which wasn't the Black Bull, was renamed earlier than the White Horse but later than the one which became the Elephant and Grasshopper, which wasn't second to receive its new name.

4 The Laughing Frog, which had not been the Rose and Crown, acquired its new name next before the pub in Grape Lane, which wasn't last to change.

5 The pub in Hops Hill made its change next after the one which became the Ticklish Trout.

	Elephant and Grasshopper	Laughing Frog	Mermaid and Dolphin	Pig and Platypus	Ticklish Trout	Barley Square	Grape Lane	Hops Hill	Malt Road	Rye Street	February	April	July	September	December
Black Bull															
Hare and Hounds															
Red Lion															
Rose and Crown															
White Horse															
February															
April															
July															
September															
December															
Barley Square															
Grape Lane															
Hops Hill															
Malt Road															
Rye Street															

Old name	New name	Location	Month

Puzzle No 35

Mobile Menace

You can't get away from mobile phones these days! Every weekday last week, Jeff Mutton was forced to listen to a conversation at close quarters. Can you work out where Jeff was on each day when the dreaded bleeping started nearby, the duration of the call on which he had to eavesdrop and who was calling the mobile owner?

Clues

1 On Tuesday Jeff was on the train when the chap opposite got a call; it was at least seven minutes longer than the call from the subscriber's secretary that he had to sit through.

2 Wednesday's call didn't disturb Jeff's restaurant meal; and that wasn't the day or the location of the shortest call, which was from someone's wife.

3 On Friday, the call was from the recipient's girlfriend; it didn't last seven minutes.

4 Jeff had to endure the seventeen-minute call on Thursday.

5 The call from Jeff's companion's mother came through while he was sitting peacefully on a park bench.

6 The call in the pub lasted for thirteen minutes.

	Park bench	Pub	Restaurant	Shop queue	Train	2 minutes	7 minutes	13 minutes	17 minutes	26 minutes	Girlfriend	Mother	Secretary	Wife	Work colleague
Monday															
Tuesday															
Wednesday															
Thursday															
Friday															
Girlfriend															
Mother															
Secretary															
Wife															
Work colleague															
2 minutes															
7 minutes															
13 minutes															
17 minutes															
26 minutes															

Day	Location	Duration of call	Caller

Puzzle No 36

Elderleigh People

Montague Elderleigh, Seventh Duke of Ellington, died in 1913 at the age of 103, having been predeceased by all six of his children, whose portraits still hang in the Drawing Room at Castle Ellington. Can you fill in the name of the person in each picture, what they became and the year of their decease?

Names: Bertha; Edward; Hannah; Henry; Irene; Samuel
Achievements: Admiral; Explorer; General; Nun; Painter; Poetess
Years of Decease: 1896; 1899; 1902; 1905; 1908; 1911

Clues
1 Henry Elderleigh passed away in 1902.
2 The explorer in the family wasn't Bertha or Edward.
3 Picture E depicts the Elderleigh who died in 1908, who wasn't Hannah.
4 Edward, whose portrait is picture B, died three years before his sister who appears in the next picture to the right.
5 Irene, who took the name Sister Modwina when she became a nun in **1872**, died earlier than her sibling shown in picture A.
6 The portrait of General Elderleigh in his full-dress uniform is two places to the right of Samuel's.
7 Portrait D shows Admiral Elderleigh on the bridge of HMS Intolerable. He didn't pass away in 1905.

A	B	C	D	E	F

Portrait	Name	Achievement	Year of decease

Starting tip:

Work out the date of death of the subject of portrait C.

Puzzle No 37

Return of the Paragon

Back in the 1930s, Charles Lieteris wrote a series of stories about Peter Galahad, alias The Paragon, a vigilante who punished criminals who were beyond the reach of the law, for *Crime Thriller* magazine; and five have just been republished in a collection, *Return of the Paragon*. Can you work out the name of the villain in each story, their crime and the date when the story originally appeared in *Crime Thriller*?

Clues

1 Max Gottfried is the villain of *The Paragon In New York*, which isn't the story first published in August 1934 in which Peter Galahad deals with a forger who plans to undermine the economic stability of the British Empire.

2 The smuggler involved in the drug and white slave trades is neither Princess Sonja nor the villain of *The Paragon Strikes Again*.

3 *The Paragon In Vienna*, in which Peter Galahad deals with a particularly despicable blackmailer, appeared in *Crime Thriller* in an earlier year than the story featuring Dr Soong, which also includes the name of a city in its title.

4 *The Paragon Against The Odds*, which originally appeared in February 1933, pits Peter against neither Igor Kagovitch nor the spy who is offering Britain's secrets to a foreign power.

5 Baron Van Damm appears in the story first published in March 1935, which wasn't *The Paragon In Cairo*.

	Baron Van Damm	Dr Soong	Igor Kagovitch	Max Gottfried	Princess Sonja	Blackmail	Forging	Jewel stealing	Smuggling	Spying	June 1932	February 1933	August 1934	March 1935	November 1935
...Against The Odds															
...In Cairo															
...In New York															
...In Vienna															
...Strikes Again															
June 1932															
February 1933															
August 1934															
March 1935															
November 1935															
Blackmail															
Forging															
Jewel stealing															
Smuggling															
Spying															

Title	Villain	Crime	Publication date

Puzzle No 38

Aye-Aye?

Long ago, when Ruritania had a navy, one of its captains sometimes took a little too much grog and got his signals mixed, causing bafflement to his crew. Can you work out in what years and on what voyage he produced five of these signals where the beginnings and ends didn't follow the normal pattern?

Clues

1 The part-order 'Keelhaul…' was given a year earlier than the one which ended '…to diving stations', but the order given by the captain bound for Rio was more than a year earlier than both.

2 'Splice…' (which wasn't accompanied by '…the mainbrace') was signalled neither in 1843 nor on the ship bound for Panama (which didn't go there in 1843).

3 The order beginning 'Hands…' was given earlier than the one issued by the captain bound for New York but later than the one ending in '…the yardarm'; none of these three orders was given in 1842.

4 'Abandon…', which wasn't followed by '…six bells', was ordered more than a year after the Cairo voyage.

5 The Bombay voyage took place one year after that in which the order beginning 'Heave…' was given, but neither of these orders was given in 1844. During one voyage, the crew were asked to heave something beginning with 'the'.

6 The order ending in '…the binnacle' was signalled in 1841.

Year	Destination	First part	Second part

Miss Raffles

Miss Raffles, criminal sister of the famous Amateur Cracksman, was missing from her usual haunts from May to September one year – but she wasn't on holiday, she was posing as a servant to a series of landowners and then, of course, decamping with their family silver. Can you work out the month in which she visited each landowner, the name of their country pile and the job Miss Raffles took whilst there?

Clues

1 Miss Raffles' unwitting employer in May was neither Lady Le Doux nor the owner of Arnesdon Castle.

2 It wasn't in September that Miss Raffles took the job as a cook, a position she occupied after – though not the month after – she worked at Fendon Abbey.

3 Miss Raffles disguised herself as a gardener's boy the month after she worked at Tipsham House, which wasn't where she worked as a secretary; neither Tipsham House nor the place where Miss Raffles posed as a gardener's boy was the family seat of Lady Babbage, who employed Miss Raffles after she had worked at these two other places.

4 Miss Raffles had already worked for two female landowners before she took the job with the woman who owns Ditchley Place.

5 The housemaid's job was held prior to the employment of Sir Arnold Wilkey, but after she had been a secretary.

6 Miss Raffles was at Lovell Hall the month after she had worked for the Duchess of Chalk and the month before she worked as a governess.

	Duchess of Chalk	Lady Babbage	Lady Le Doux	Lord Shipton	Sir Arnold Wilkey	Arnesdon Castle	Ditchley Place	Fendon Abbey	Lovell Hall	Tipsham House	Cook	Gardener's boy	Governess	Housemaid	Secretary
May															
June															
July															
August															
September															
Cook											
Gardener's boy											
Governess											
Housemaid											
Secretary											
Arnesdon Castle						
Ditchley Place						
Fendon Abbey						
Lovell Hall						
Tipsham House						

Month	Landowner	House	Job

Puzzle No 40

Travelling Bags

Five air travellers were annoyed to discover that their luggage had gone to a destination far removed from that to which they were travelling. Can you say where each was going, for what reason and name the place where each person's luggage was sent?

Clues

1 The man who flew to Vienna wasn't Mr Jett, whose luggage was eventually tracked down in Cairo.

2 The bags which should have gone to Rome didn't end up in Bombay. The owner of the luggage which did go to Bombay wasn't flying to pay a family visit.

3 Mrs Fare was flying out to attend her daughter's wedding. Her outfit which went missing wasn't in the luggage which should have gone to New York but which was sent instead to Nairobi.

4 The name of the person whose luggage was found in Venice occurs earlier in the alphabetical list than that of the one whose cases ended up in Paris.

5 Mr Flyer's journey was to Madrid; his luggage was sent to another European city.

6 The business conference to which one passenger was travelling was held in Frankfurt.

7 Mr Case wasn't the passenger going on a week's holiday, whose name isn't next but one in the alphabetical list to that of the one taking a weekend break.

	Frankfurt	Madrid	New York	Rome	Vienna	Attending wedding	Business conference	Family visit	Holiday	Weekend break	Bombay	Cairo	Nairobi	Paris	Venice
Mr Case															
Mrs Fare															
Mr Flyer															
Mr Jett															
Miss Ticket															
Bombay											
Cairo											
Nairobi											
Paris											
Venice											
Attending wedding						
Business conference						
Family visit						
Holiday						
Weekend break						

Passenger	Destination	Reason	Luggage sent to

Puzzle No 41

All Aboard

The diagram shows six coaches in the car-park of a stately home. Each has brought a party of foreign tourists, every party being from a different country. Can you name the driver of each of the coaches lettered A to F and work out how many passengers of what nationality each has brought to visit the house? NB – Left and right refer throughout the clues to the diagram as you look at it.

Clues

1 Alan's coach is immediately left of the one carrying the Americans and immediately right of the one which had 63 on board when it arrived.

2 Desmond is driving the Japanese party; their coach isn't parked next to the one which has a passenger list numbering 67.

3 Coach D's complement of passengers is four higher than that of Lewis' coach.

4 The fewest number of tourists have arrived on coach A, whose passengers aren't French.

5 The 69 Indian tourists came in a coach now parked somewhere to the left of the one driven by Roger, but not next to it.

6 The Dutch tourists currently being shown round the house are from coach E; they aren't the party of 66, whose coach is parked next to the one driven by Douglas, whose passengers aren't 65 in number.

	Alan	Carl	Desmond	Douglas	Lewis	Roger	American	Austrian	Dutch	French	Indian	Japanese	61 passengers	63 passengers	65 passengers	66 passengers	67 passengers	69 passengers
Coach A																		
Coach B																		
Coach C																			
Coach D																			
Coach E																			
Coach F																			

Puzzle No 42

Ubiquitous Ursula

Ursula Orlovah is the most frequently seen personality on Balonian television. In the course of one day last week, she appeared on six different channels. Can you fill in her schedule in the table?

Channels: 1; 3; 4; 6; 7; 8
Programmes: *A Good Start*; *Computer Fun*, *Give Us A Hint*; *Hellidays*; *Value For Money*; *Winner Takes All*

Clues

1 The channel number of lottery programme *Winner Takes All* is one lower than that of the 5.30pm programme, but one higher than that of the 4.00pm one.

2 *Computer Fun* is screened earlier than Ursula's channel 7 programme but later than her channel 4 one.

3 Ursula appeared on channel 8 two hours later than on her pre-school programme *A Good Start*; the latter's channel number is one higher than that of the panel game *Give Us A Hint*, on which Ursula was a contestant and which went out earlier than *A Good Start*.

4 The programme *Hellidays* in which Ursula interviews survivors of holiday disasters doesn't have the latest time or the highest channel number, but is screened later than her channel 3 programme.

5 Her consumer watchdog programme *Value For Money* (whose channel number is lower than that of her 12.30 programme) wasn't the last of her day's appearances.

Time	Channel	Programme
12.30		
2.00		
3.30		
4.00		
5.30		
6.00		

Starting tip:

Work out which programme was broadcast at 6.00pm.

- 43 -

Puzzle No 43

Cabbages and Kings?

The four old men who regularly sat on the park bench spoke of many things. Yesterday, their conversation was dominated by four topics, each introduced by a different member of the quartet. Can you indicate each man, his name and age, the topic he had led the way on and the order in which these subjects were discussed?

Names: Charles; David; Norman; Peter
Ages: 76; 78; 80; 82
Topics: Health Service; modern youth; pensions; television standards

Clues
1 Norman was further left than, but not next to, the man who complained about sex and violence on television, who raised this topic before Norman's complaint and who is two years younger than Norman.
2 David is four years younger than the man who found fault with modern youth and who was next to and left of David.
3 The man in position A, who isn't Charles, raised his topic next after the 82-year-old.
4 The 80-year-old sat next to and right of the man who grumbled about the Health Service and spoke next but one after him.
5 The man who led a spirited attack on the inadequacy of pensions spoke next after the man at D who didn't speak first; he is older than both the latter and Peter.
6 The man who introduced the second topic sat next to the one who introduced the fourth topic, who is more than two years older than the one who introduced the second.

A   B   C   D

Position	Name	Age	Topic	Order

Starting tip:

First work out what man D spoke of and then name the 82-year-old.

Puzzle No 44

Bed and Breakfast

Vince and Jenny were on a cycling holiday, spending each night in a different Youth Hostel. Can you name the hostels in the order in which they were visited, say how many guests there were staying there on the night Vince and Jenny were in residence and name the breakfast dish served up to Vince and Jenny on the following morning at each hostel?

Clues

1 Muesli, which was eaten some time after the cornflakes, wasn't on offer at All Comers, which lived up to its name by catering for 80 guests on the night (not the fifth) that Vince and Jenny stayed there.

2 The couple stayed at Old Hallows on the second night of their holiday.

3 A total of 50 guests were present for breakfast when Vince and Jenny had the sausages; this was on one of the odd-numbered visits.

4 The third hostel our duo stayed at had 65 guests on that night.

5 Pembury Castle had fewer visitors than both the hostel where Vince and Jenny ate scrambled egg for breakfast and the one they stayed at on the fourth night and was visited earlier than the latter.

6 There were 15 more guests at Adcaster Mill than at the hostel where Vince and Jenny sampled the baked beans.

	Adcaster Mill	All Comers	Monckton Hall	Old Hallows	Pembury Castle	15	30	50	65	80	Baked beans	Cornflakes	Muesli	Sausages	Scrambled egg
First															
Second															
Third															
Fourth															
Fifth															
Baked beans															
Cornflakes															
Muesli															
Sausages															
Scrambled egg															
15															
30															
50															
65															
80															

Order	Hostel	Guests	Breakfast

Puzzle No 45

Wish We Weren't Here

Each weekday last week a postcard arrived from a married couple on holiday, each one complaining about the weather or the resort or the accommodation. Can you work out who is married to whom, on what day each couple's card arrived and where each couple were spending their holiday?

Clues

1 The card from Verna came a day later than the one from John but a day earlier than the one from Italy.

2 Sarah travelled abroad, but not with Nigel or the man whose card arrived on Wednesday.

3 The card from Scotland arrived the day before the one from Greece; neither of these was from either Bev or George.

4 The couple who took their holiday in England are the only ones whose names have the same number of letters as each other; their card was delivered later than either Alison's or the one from Spain.

5 George's card arrived earlier than Mike's, which was two days ahead of Paula's; Garry didn't go to Italy.

Day	Wife	Husband	Holiday place

Puzzle No 46

Happy Daze

The Witt family likes to mark every event with a puzzle and one of their favourites was the Advent Calendar game where a different letter of the alphabet was revealed every day. This one, devised by Grandma Nita, is about young Harv learning to drive.

The letters in TRAFFIC had all appeared by the 17th but no earlier. The MOTORWAY, one letter appearing on the 3rd, was completed on the 22nd, two days before the JUNCTION, so of course also on the 24th a QUEUE formed. On the 18th, but no earlier, he'd learnt to use his MIRROR, one letter being on the 13th and on the 21st, again no earlier, he'd mastered OVERTAKING, two consecutive letters of which fell on the 1st and the 8th.

The letters of LANE read in reverse order (though not necessarily consecutively).

The five vowels appeared in four columns but not Monday or Tuesday. The A and the O were in the same column. The TEST had to wait until the 26th before it could be completed, naturally the same date produced a PASS.

Apart from I and J which are diagonally adjacent, no letters consecutive in the alphabet are adjacent in any direction, including diagonally, nor are they in the same column (A and Z are regarded as consecutive). The ZEBRA was crossed by the 23rd but no earlier and the Z didn't appear on a Monday. VEHICLE was completed on the 25th but no earlier and the dates of V and I added together equal the date of H. The date of X is divisible by 5. L is on a row somewhere above Y. One letter of DRIVING fell on the 19th. M squared equals Q and the total of the dates of CAR equal O.

Can you fill in the calendar?

Monday	Tuesday	Wednesday	Thursday	Friday	Saturday	Sunday
	1	2	3	4	5	6
7	8	9	10	11	12	13
14	15	16	17	18	19	20
21	22	23	24	25	26	

Puzzle No 47

Livingstone St, I Presume

The diagram shows a network of streets in the centre of town. The owners of the shops numbered 1 to 6, each in a similar position in a different side-street, all belong to the local traders' association. Can you work out the name and trade of the owner of each shop and name the street in which it is situated?

Clues

1 Gregson's carpet emporium isn't in either of the easternmost streets.

2 The number indicating the post office, which isn't in Victoria Street, is either three higher or three lower than that of Mr Lewis' shop.

3 Shop number 1 is in Livingstone Street; its proprietor's name immediately follows in the alphabetical list that of the man who runs the off-licence numbered 5 in the diagram.

4 Bull's shop bears a number two lower than that of Myers' business in Morton Street; the former isn't in David Street, which isn't the address of shop number 4.

5 The chemist's shop in Henry Street isn't shop number 6.

6 Jordan's shop is number 2 on the plan.

7 The antiques shop isn't the business of Mr Spencer.

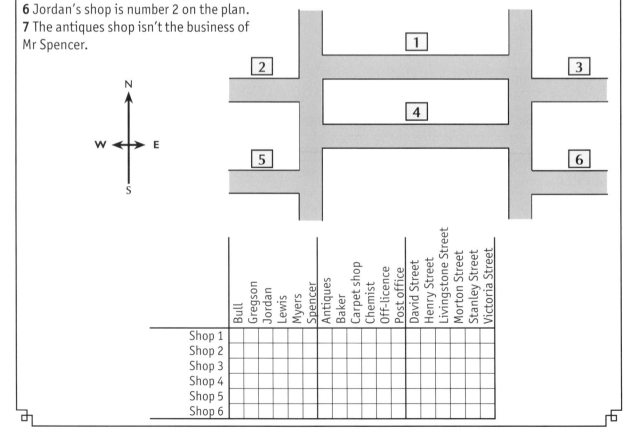

	Bull	Gregson	Jordan	Lewis	Myers	Spencer	Antiques	Baker	Carpet shop	Chemist	Off-licence	Post office	David Street	Henry Street	Livingstone Street	Morton Street	Stanley Street	Victoria Street
Shop 1																		
Shop 2																		
Shop 3																		
Shop 4																		
Shop 5																		
Shop 6																		

Length is Strength

Four bridge players, seated in the traditional positions North, South, East and West (the two former being partners against the two latter), each picked up a hand with a different long suit, but a different length in each case. Can you name the player in each seat, match him with his long suit and say how many cards of that suit he held?

Names: Bidding; Pass; Ruff; Trumpet
Suits: Clubs; diamonds; hearts; spades
Length: 5; 6; 7; 8

Clues

1 Ruff had more of his suit than his partner had in clubs, which was his long suit.

2 Trumpet had a suit longer than that of the player who held the long diamonds.

3 South's long suit had only five cards in it.

4 East's suit was hearts.

5 Pass was the player in the North seat.

6 It was Bidding's partner at the table who had the longest suit of all.

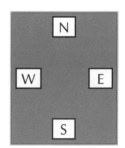

Position	Name	Suit	Length

Starting tip:

Begin by working out Ruff's seat.

Puzzle No 49

Islands in the Sun

Four couples booked holidays on different islands for themselves and their two children. Can you match the couples, work out their surnames and the names of their children and say which island paradise each foursome visited?

Clues

1 Rebecca is Charles' sister.

2 Keith and Angela's son isn't the boy named Darren Morris.

3 Judy Langton's holiday location wasn't Cyprus and her son's name isn't Ian.

4 Chris is Garry's father and Gail is the daughter of Lance, who didn't visit the Canaries.

5 Violet is Fiona's mother; she isn't married to Perry and she isn't Mrs Chadwick, who holidayed in Crete.

6 Bridget and her husband took their children to Majorca.

Husband	Wife	Surname	Son	Daughter	Location

Puzzle No 50

Logical Moves

Five holidaymakers encountered different problems with their hotel rooms. The manager met all the complaints by allocating to each guest a room vacated by one of the others. Can you match names with complaints, say which room each was moved to and name the person to whom it had been originally assigned? NB – The first number of each room designates the floor on which it is situated.

Clues

1 The person who suffers from vertigo was moved from the fifth floor room numbered 512 to room 120 on the first floor.

2 A guest who was slightly deaf was switched to the room previously occupied by Stephen, who had been kept awake by loud snoring from an adjacent room.

3 Jennifer, whose original room was 237, was moved into the one vacated by Marjorie.

4 Howard, whose complaint wasn't the lack of a sea view, was given a fourth floor room as his replacement accommodation.

5 The guest who complained of the noise from the disco next door to the hotel was given the room originally allocated to Colin, which was on an odd-numbered floor.

6 No two guests were involved in a direct exchange of rooms.

	Disco noise	No sea view	Smell from kitchens	Snoring	Vertigo	Room 120	Room 237	Room 334	Room 421	Room 512	Colin	Howard	Jennifer	Marjorie	Stephen
Colin															
Howard															
Jennifer															
Marjorie															
Stephen															
Colin															
Howard															
Jennifer															
Marjorie															
Stephen															
Room 120															
Room 237															
Room 334															
Room 421															
Room 512															

Holidaymaker	Problem	New room	Previous occupant

Puzzle No 51

Pop Classics

From time to time the Netherlipp Music Society slips an unconventional item into its normal classical repertoire and last month's meeting was just such an occasion. The item was a Beatles medley and featured six soloists, who sat in front of the orchestra. Can you say which instrumentalist sat at which place, which number each played as a solo and in what order these solos were played?

Instruments: Cello; clarinet; flute; horn; oboe; violin
Songs: *A Hard Day's Night; Eleanor Rigby; Penny Lane; Strawberry Fields; Yellow Submarine; Yesterday*

Clues
1 No-one's seat matched the order in which he or she played, eg the person in A didn't play first, etc.
2 The flautist sat next to and right of the person who played *A Hard Day's Night*, whose solo came more than one place before the flute solo.
3 The *Yesterday* soloist played next after the person in seat A; neither is the violinist. Neither the violinist nor the cellist played *Yellow Submarine*, which came next after the number from the musician in chair D.
4 The *Eleanor Rigby* soloist sat next to and left of the one who played fourth; the horn player, who was neither of these, performed next after the cellist, who was immediately to his or her left.
5 The player of *Penny Lane* was next to and right of the violinist and performed more than one place later. The oboist gave his solo two places before (and sat more than one place to the right of) the cellist.

6 *Strawberry Fields* came later than two of the three woodwind (clarinet, flute and oboe) solos and next before that of the other woodwind. The player in seat E performed next after the one in C, but the clarinet solo was more than one place before either.

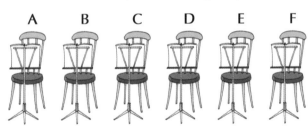

| A | B | C | D | E | F |

Seat	Instrument	Number played	Order

Starting tip:

Work out what C and E are playing and then find the first song.

- 53 -

Puzzle No 52

Mountain Manoeuvres

A party of mountaineers from the British Army has just climbed the infamous Mount Adamrest in the Herelayes range. Can you work out the rank, name and military unit of each climber and the rôle he or she undertook on the expedition?

Clues

1 As he or she is of the most senior rank, it was the Lieutenant who served as team leader.

2 Andy Clive, who wasn't the cook, is a Corporal.

3 Fiona Havelock is serving in the Royal Logistics Corps.

4 The Royal Artillery is the only unit in the Army which uses the rank of Gunner.

5 The expedition's female medical specialist is a member of the Royal Army Medical Corps.

	Andy Clive	Fiona Havelock	Kate McMahon	Simon Wolfe	Royal Army Medical Corps	Royal Artillery	Royal Engineers	Royal Logistics Corps	Cook	Medic	Radio operator	Team leader
Corporal												
Gunner												
Lieutenant												
Sergeant												
Cook									
Medic									
Radio operator									
Team leader									
RA Medical Corps				
Royal Artillery				
Royal Engineers				
Royal Logistics Corps				

Rank	Name	Unit	Rôle

Puzzle No 53

Shopping for Lunch

Four of the women from the office of Spendmore & Co went shopping in their lunch-hour and each bought something for her forthcoming summer holiday. Can you work out which store she went to, what she purchased and its size?

Clues

1 Neither the shopper who bought the size 10 garment from Last nor Heather (who shopped at Atem) bought the bright red minidress to wear on holiday.

2 The stonewashed denim jeans are a size 12.

3 The swimsuit is of a larger size than Nikki's purchase.

4 Sarah's new size 14 garment didn't come from D&B.

5 Diane bought herself a long pinafore dress to cover up a bit (or a lot!) in the sun.

	Atem	D&B	Ebenham's	Last	Jeans	Minidress	Pinafore dress	Swimsuit	10	12	14	16
Diane												
Heather												
Nikki												
Sarah												
10												
12												
14												
16												
Jeans												
Minidress												
Pinafore dress												
Swimsuit												

Shopper	Shop	Garment	Size

Puzzle No 54

Spice Girls Memories

No, not a singing group but about four friends who were at Storbury Upper School together in the early 90s and met the other day at a reunion. (I suppose it's fairly obvious why they got their nicknames.) Can you work out each girl's full name, what she was best at in her schooldays and what she's doing now?

Clues

1 Ms Turmerick's first name is the same length as the fashion model's; and neither was good at foreign languages in her schooldays.

2 Miss Cynamon is an assistant in a department store.

3 Gail's surname was – indeed, still is – Nuttmeg.

4 The former school hockey captain is now a journalist with the Storbury Free Press.

5 Laura won prizes for English when she was a pupil at the Upper School.

6 Miss Pepper, whose art teacher thought she had the potential to become a professional painter, isn't Toni.

	Cynamon	Nuttmeg	Pepper	Turmerick	English	Hockey	Languages	Painting	Journalist	Model	Shop assistant	Teacher
Celia												
Gail												
Laura												
Toni												
Journalist												
Model												
Shop assistant												
Teacher												
English												
Hockey												
Languages												
Painting												

Forename	Surname	Best subject	Occupation

Puzzle No 55

Battle of Wits

Each of the squares numbered 1 to 12 contains the date of a battle famous in British history. Can you place each in its correct square? When you have completed the problem, just for fun, see how many of the battles you can name in the table given. The answers are given with the solution.

Dates: 1066; 1314; 1415; 1642; 1704; 1746; 1759; 1805; 1815; 1916; 1940; 1942.

Clues

1 The date of the Battle of Hastings (1066) appears in square 6.
2 Reading from top to bottom, one column has three dates in chronological order, ending with 1805.
3 An exact number of hundreds of years separate the dates in squares 4 and 10.
4 Column C contains two 20th-century dates, but there is no 20th-century date in column D.
5 The year in square 12 ends in an even digit; it is a later year in the same century as its neighbour in square 11.
6 The year 1940 is in the square immediately next to and right of the one containing 1759.
7 Square 8 contains the next date chronologically following the one in square 9.

A	B	C	D
✖ 1	✖ 2	✖ 3	✖ 4
✖ 5	✖ 6	✖ 7	✖ 8
✖ 9	✖ 10	✖ 11	✖ 12

Just for fun ...

1066 HASTINGS	1314	1415	1642
1704	1746	1759	1805
1815	1916	1940	1942

Starting tip:

Work out which column is referred to in clue 2.

- 57 -

Home Town Politics

Some people in Blotvia have names deriving from their city of origin: Vilski, for instance, means 'from Vilsk'. There are five men with names of this type in the new parliament but none sits for the town from which his name derives. From the clues given below (and this introduction) can you work out each man's full name, party and constituency?

Clues

1 Mr Zivazi is a member of the Liberal Party; the Radical Member of the Blotvian Parliament doesn't represent Hatrov.

2 Nikolai is MBP for Pulak; Vasili's constituency isn't Elsk.

3 Boris Elski isn't MBP for Crim.

4 Sergei isn't the Nationalist, who is neither Mr Hatrovi nor the representative for Hatrov.

5 Dmitri, the Democratic MBP, is the only one of the five who represents a party with the same initial letter as his first name; his constituency isn't Elsk.

6 Mr Pulaki represents Zivaz in the Blotvian Parliament, but Mr Zivazi doesn't represent Pulak.

Forename	Surname	Party	Constituency

Puzzle No 57

The Quick and Thurstead

There have been a lot of complaints about speeding motorists from the villagers of Thurstead, near Storbury, so last Saturday, the police turned up in force and managed to apprehend five offenders. Can you work out what type of car each speeder was driving, what speed they were doing and where in the village they were doing it?

Clues

1 The Volvo 460 driver was charged with speeding in Bridge Street, in the middle of the village's 30mph zone.

2 The Ford Escort was travelling at 50mph, which wasn't as fast as Patsy O'Meta's car.

3 Vince Well's car was travelling at 70mph just before he was pulled up by a police patrol car.

4 Andy Boate's car was spotted in Storbury Road, travelling twenty miles per hour faster than the Rover Metro.

5 Neither Ken Limit nor the motorist charged with speeding up Gallows Hill was driving a Ford.

6 It was in Plough Lane that one motorist was seen driving at 60mph.

	Ford Escort	Ford Mondeo	Honda Accord	Rover Metro	Volvo 460	40mph	50mph	60mph	70mph	80mph	Bridge Street	Church Lane	Gallows Hill	Plough Lane	Storbury Road
Andy Boate															
Doris Copp															
Ken Limit															
Patsy O'Meta															
Vince Well															
Bridge Street															
Church Lane															
Gallows Hill															
Plough Lane															
Storbury Road															
40mph															
50mph															
60mph															
70mph															
80mph															

Driver	Car	Speed	Location

Home on the Kibbutz

Five men who have emigrated to Israel work on the same kibbutz. Can you fully identify the five, say in which order they arrived at the kibbutz and name the country from which they emigrated?

Clues

1 David was the next man to take up his place at the kibbutz after Levin, who had emigrated from Russia.

2 Leon Cohen wasn't the second man to arrive.

3 The fifth emigrant to begin work at the kibbutz was Aaron, who has not come to Israel from Canada and whose surname isn't Black.

4 The Englishman was the fourth to be welcomed by his fellow-workers on the kibbutz.

5 The surname of the first of the five men to arrive was Goldstein; he isn't Simon.

6 Daniel joined the kibbutz after leaving his friends and family in the United States.

	Black	Blomberg	Cohen	Goldstein	Levin	First	Second	Third	Fourth	Fifth	Canada	England	Poland	Russia	USA
Aaron															
Daniel															
David															
Leon															
Simon															
Canada															
England															
Poland															
Russia															
USA															
First															
Second															
Third															
Fourth															
Fifth															

First name	Surname	Order of arrival	From

Puzzle No 59

Props

The property mistress for the local amateur theatre group has several important placings of props on stage during Act 1 of its latest production. Can you work out the setting for each scene, the object that must be on stage and where it is to be located?

Clues

1 The bottle and glasses aren't the props for Scene 1, which isn't in the bedroom.

2 The location for the prop in Scene 2 is the window-sill.

3 A book is required in Scene 3, which isn't set in the study.

4 For Scene 4, which takes place in the hall, the prop isn't the bottle and glasses and shouldn't be placed on the cupboard; nor is scene 4 the one when the cigarettes are to be placed on the mantelpiece.

5 The pot-plant is the prop for the garden scene.

6 The prop for the study scene needs to be placed on the coffee-table.

	Bedroom	Drawing-room	Garden	Hall	Study	Book	Bottle and glasses	Cigarettes	Gloves	Pot-plant	Chair	Coffee-table	Cupboard	Mantelpiece	Window-sill
Scene 1															
Scene 2															
Scene 3															
Scene 4															
Scene 5															
Chair															
Coffee-table															
Cupboard															
Mantelpiece															
Window-sill															
Book															
Bottle and glasses															
Cigarettes															
Gloves															
Pot-plant															

Scene	Setting	Prop	Location

Puzzle No 60

Holy Order

Eight baptisms were performed at fortnightly intervals by the vicar at St Saviour's Church. Can you match the dates in the baptismal roll with the name and surname of the child Christened on each occasion?

Forenames: Anne; Anthony; Edward; Eleanor; Emma; Geraldine; James; Mark
Surnames: Christian; Cross; Dove; Font; Godfather; Jordan; Parsons; Waters

Clues

1 The forenames of the infants baptised on March 1st and May 10th have the same initial letter.
2 Parsons is the next surname in the roll after Geraldine's.
3 The first baby to appear on the baptismal roll is Mr and Mrs Cross's new daughter.
4 Emma was baptised exactly four weeks before the boy surnamed Christian.
5 Anne was baptised on the 15th of a month in which James, who doesn't share a surname initial in common with that of any other baby, was also Christened.
6 Baby Font was baptised next after baby Godfather and next before Mark.
7 Eleanor, whose surname isn't Dove, was Christened in the same month as the child surnamed Jordan.

St Saviour's Roll of Baptisms 2005

Date	Forename	Surname
February 1st		
February 15th		
March 1st		
March 15th		
March 29th		
April 12th		
April 26th		
May 10th		

Starting tip:

Puzzle No 61

The Y Files

FBI Special Agents Mildew and Scilly have been called to five more mysterious occurrences in the USA. Can you discover the town, state and exact time when each investigation began and the nature of the phenomenon being investigated?

Clues

1 The glowing forest was located in Montana, but not near Weirdsville or Strangeleigh and the investigation didn't commence at 11.32am; Mildew and Scilly were also not at Weirdsville at 11.32am.

2 The Strangeleigh investigation began at 2.07pm, but it didn't concern mysteriously disappearing families.

3 The Ohio case began at 10.31am, but not in Weirdsville.

4 The wreckage in the desert wasn't in Kansas.

5 The crater in the mountainside was near the town of Bizarre, while Mildew and Scilly began their investigation of the lights in the sky at 6.48am.

6 One investigation took place in Enigma, Oregon.

	Kansas	Montana	New Mexico	Ohio	Oregon	6.48am	10.31am	11.32am	2.07pm	4.16pm	Crater in mountainside	Disappearing families	Glowing forest	Lights in sky	Wreckage in desert
Arkane															
Bizarre															
Enigma															
Strangeleigh															
Weirdsville															
Crater in m'side															
Disappearing fam															
Glowing forest															
Lights in sky															
Wreckage in desert															
6.48am															
10.31am															
11.32am															
2.07pm															
4.16pm															

Town	State	Time	Phenomenon

Puzzle No 62

Prodigal Prodigies

The musical parents of five musical daughters were very keen for the latter to make their mark in the musical world, but were doomed to disappointment when they each took up non-musical careers, four of them taking up residence abroad. Can you match each of the girls with the musical area in which she excelled and say what she does now and where she is based?

Clues

1 Nancy was the only one who maintained even a vague connection with music, becoming a theatrical agent.

2 Joan was the youthful flautist.

3 The young woman now living in New York, who wasn't a violinist in childhood, has a name one letter longer than that of her sister in Moscow.

4 The clarinettist is the only daughter currently based in the UK; she works in London, but isn't the diplomat, who has a foreign posting.

5 The childhood piano-player is now exercising her linguistic talents as a courier.

6 Anna now works in Paris.

7 Moira, who isn't a journalist, lives in a European capital city.

8 One sister became a geologist and is based in Rome.

	Clarinet	Flute	Piano	Singing	Violin	London	Moscow	New York	Paris	Rome	Courier	Diplomat	Geologist	Journalist	Theatrical agent
Anna															
Joan															
Kathleen															
Moira															
Nancy															
Courier															
Diplomat															
Geologist															
Journalist															
Theatrical agent															
London															
Moscow															
New York															
Paris															
Rome															

Name	Talent	Location	Job

Puzzle No 63

Expert Opinion

Five experts were giving their opinions on various items brought by members of the public to be assessed on a TV antiques programme. Can you identify the five, say which is their special area of expertise and work out in which order they were first seen on the programme, which, of course, switches from one to another as the show progresses?

Clues

1 Ernest Dell was first seen by viewers immediately before the doll expert.

2 Lavinia's area of expertise is porcelain.

3 The third resident expert to be featured by the producer on this week's show was the one named Highfield.

4 Jonathan was the expert seen voicing his opinion at the beginning of the programme.

5 The first glimpse of the expert named Pride was when he was giving an opinion on a pair of duelling pistols; this was during the next slot in the programme after the one occupied by Carrow.

6 A silver teapot was the object given second billing on this week's programme.

	Carrow	Dell	Goodison	Highfield	Pride	Dolls	Firearms	Furniture	Porcelain	Silver	First	Second	Third	Fourth	Fifth
Angus															
Ernest															
Jonathan															
Lavinia															
Tessa															
First															
Second															
Third															
Fourth															
Fifth															
Dolls															
Firearms															
Furniture															
Porcelain															
Silver															

Forename	Surname	Expertise	Order

- 65 -

Puzzle No 64

Mothers' Day

It's Mothers' Day and five lucky mums, each with a son and daughter, have received special treats on their special day. From the information given, can you discover which son and daughter belong to each mum and the treat each planned?

Clues

1 Mark and Laura are brother and sister, but neither Thomas nor James is Sarah's brother; Thomas and his sister took their mother breakfast in bed.

2 James isn't Jan's son and her daughter's name begins with an L.

3 Pat is George's mum. Lucy and her brother took their mum a cup of tea in bed.

4 The children who cooked lunch were neither Katy nor James; they aren't Carol's children and she wasn't the recipient of the lunch.

5 Katy isn't Brenda's daughter and George didn't wash up.

6 Gemma is Sandra's daughter.

Mum	Son	Daughter	Treat

Puzzle No 65

Sick Soldiers

The Medical Officer of that grand old British infantry regiment the 13th Foot and Mouth holds sick parade every morning, even though there are unlikely to be any major casualties – after all, the regiment is currently stationed in Aldershot. Can you fill in the name of each soldier waiting to see the MO and say what's wrong with him? NB – Soldier No 1 is at the front of the queue and No 6 is at the back.

Soldiers: Battle; Busby, Fortress; Martial; Rampart; Troop
Complaints: Boil; bruised toe; cut finger; earache; sore throat; stomach ache

Clues

1 Private Battle will see the MO some time before the soldier with the sore throat, who is standing two places ahead of Private Rampart.

2 The man in position 4 has a longer surname than the soldier with earache, who is next to and ahead of Private Fortress.

3 The man with a boil on his – anyway, he's got a boil – is standing next to and ahead of the soldier with a bruised toe and next to and behind Private Martial.

4 Private Troop, who cut his finger while peeling potatoes, is standing two places ahead of the soldier with stomach ache.

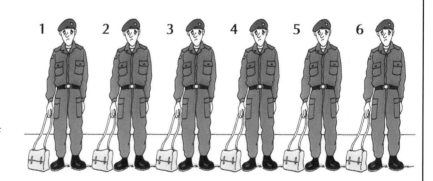

Position	Soldier	Complaint

Starting tip:

Puzzle No 66

In Triplicate

Albion TV is putting together a documentary about triplets and a researcher has found five sets of triplets willing to take part. Can you work out the first names and surname of each set? (The first names are listed in order of age – though the senior in each case is only minutes older than the youngest; coincidentally, all the female triplets still use their maiden names.)

Clues

1 Lydia isn't one of the Quinn triplets, the eldest of whom is female.

2 Dinah isn't related to Marie Smith.

3 Beryl and Gavin are sister and brother, but aren't related to Marie.

4 Joyce Perry is no relation to Colin and his sister Nancy.

5 Irene has a brother just three minutes younger than she is. Henry (whose surname isn't Tyler) has a brother who is older by five minutes.

6 Alice Rudge isn't related to Frank or Keith.

		Middle					Youngest									
		Frank	Gavin	Henry	Irene	Joyce	Keith	Lydia	Marie	Nancy	Oscar	Perry	Quinn	Rudge	Smith	Tyler
ELDEST	Alice															
	Beryl															
	Colin															
	Dinah															
	Edwin															
	Perry															
	Quinn															
	Rudge															
	Smith															
	Tyler															
	Keith															
	Lydia															
	Marie															
	Nancy															
	Oscar															

Eldest	Middle	Youngest	Surname

Puzzle No 67

Flying a Kite

The diagram shows four children flying their kites on the common. Can you name the child flying each of the kites lettered A to D and work out his or her age and identify the colour of the kite he or she is flying?

Children: Henry; Jack; Kate; Marie
Ages: 8; 9; 10; 11
Colours: Blue; orange; red; yellow

Clues

1 The oldest and youngest of the children are next to each other in the diagram. Neither is Henry, whose kite is orange.

2 Kite B is red; the child flying it is two years older than Katie.

3 The child aged 9 is flying the blue kite, which isn't lettered D.

4 Jack, who isn't flying kite A, isn't as old as Marie.

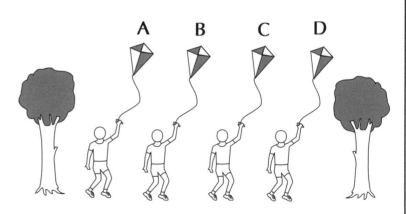

Position	Child	Age	Colour

Starting tip:

Puzzle No 68

Egon Toste

Famous restaurant critic Egon Toste has just published his latest guide. Below are details of one restaurant in each of the five star ratings. Can you discover the name of the chef at each restaurant, how many stars were awarded there and the dish particularly recommended by Mr Toste?

Clues

1 Gorsehill Manor was awarded more than three stars, where the recommended dish isn't lemon surprise; it was also not the restaurant where chef Toby Cameron served the superb beef Wellington.

2 Toni Giordano's restaurant bears his name; it didn't receive three stars and again the special dish isn't the lemon surprise.

3 Antoine Marron's establishment was awarded two stars.

4 Arcadia received only one star; the chef there isn't Philippe Legrand, whose speciality dish isn't ragout of lamb.

5 The Vineyard Restaurant is famous for its game pie, but it is prepared by neither Pierre Laval nor Philippe Legrand.

6 The four-star restaurant serves the pears in port. The three-star restaurant doesn't serve the surprise.

	Antoine Marron	Philippe Legrand	Pierre Laval	Toby Cameron	Toni Giordano	1 star	2 stars	3 stars	4 stars	5 stars	Beef Wellington	Game pie	Lemon surprise	Pears in port	Ragout of lamb
Arcadia															
Giordano's															
Gorsehill Manor															
La Pergola															
The Vineyard															
Beef Wellington															
Game pie															
Lemon surprise															
Pears in port															
Ragout of lamb															
1 star															
2 stars															
3 stars															
4 stars															
5 stars															

Restaurant	Chef	No of stars	Dish

Starbattles

In the *Starbattle* series of films, heroic rebel leader Mark Voidfarer confronts – and ultimately defeats, of course – a number of evil representatives of the corrupt Star Empire. Can you work out the name of the villain (or villainess) of each film, the particular weapon each uses against Mark's rebels and how they get their comeuppance in the closing sequences of the film?

Clues

1 General Zorkh, who dies in a powersword fight with Mark on the battlements of Fort Doomstar, isn't the baddie whose forces armed with the Disintegrator Gun oppose the rebels in the first of the five films.

2 Lady Cathadon and her army of mutant warriors don't appear in *Starbattle II*.

3 The male villain who is shot down in a starfighter dogfight with Mark features in *Starbattle III*, but the multi-tentacled alien mercenaries don't.

4 It isn't in *Starbattle IV* that the leading baddie perishes in an exploding starcruiser while trying to flee the victorious rebels.

5 The male villain of *Starbattle V* isn't the employer of the alien mercenaries.

6 Princess Kalka, evil daughter of the Star Emperor himself, isn't the leader of the legion of killer robots who finally commits suicide by leaping from a cliff rather than face Mark Voidfarer's vengeful rebels.

7 The dastardly Duke Darvad isn't the baddie whose forces are armed with a Mind Control Ray capable of ... well, controlling people's minds, really.

	Duke Darvad	General Zorkh	Lady Cathadon	Prince Gordan	Princess Kalka	Alien mercenaries	Disintegrator Gun	Killer robots	Mind Control Ray	Mutant warriors	Jumps off cliff	Planet explodes	Powersword fight	Starcruiser explodes	Starfighter dogfight
Starbattle I															
Starbattle II															
Starbattle III															
Starbattle IV															
Starbattle V															
Jumps off cliff															
Planet explodes															
Powersword fight															
Starcruiser explodes															
Starfighter dogfight															
Alien mercenaries															
Disintegrator Gun															
Killer robots															
Mind Control Ray															
Mutant warriors															

Film	Villain	Weapon	Fate

Puzzle No 70

Flatmates

Six elderly married couples live in sheltered accommodation with warden support in the flats numbered 1 to 6 in the diagram. Can you fully identify the couple who live in each flat?

Clues

1 Albert and Violet live in the flat immediately above that occupied by the Simpsons.

2 Margaret Dixon shares an even-numbered flat with her husband.

3 The surname of the couple in flat 4 isn't Lewis.

4 Flat 6 belongs to John and his wife.

5 Madge and her husband live in flat 5; he isn't Donald Williams, who has a flat on the same floor as that of Mr and Mrs Robins.

6 The Gordons' flat bears a number one higher than Leonard's.

7 Bernard's flat is directly above Joan's.

8 Henry isn't married to Sarah.

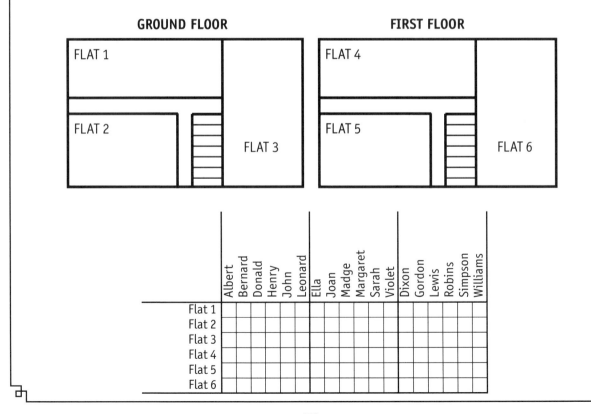

- 72 -

Puzzle No 71

By the Seaside

The diagram shows four children paddling in the sea, while their respective mothers sit in deck-chairs on the beach keeping a watchful eye on them. Can you identify the four children lettered A to D and the four mothers numbered 1 to 4 and match them up correctly?

Children: Damien; Emma; Jack; Karen
Mothers: Francesca; Jill; Lesley; Sally

Clues

1 None of the children is indicated by a letter whose position in the alphabet is equivalent to the number denoting his or her mother.

2 As they sit facing out to sea Jill is immediately to the right of Emma's mum and immediately to the left of the mother of child D.

3 Jack is the son of Francesca, who isn't in deck-chair 3.

4 Karen is paddling two positions to the left (facing the sea) of Lesley's child.

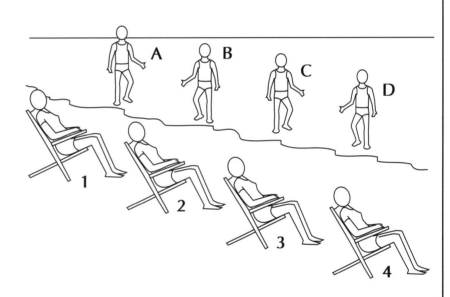

Child	Child's name	Mother	Mother's name

Starting tip:

First work out in which chair the mother of child D is sitting.

Puzzle No 72

Love Pays the bills

Teacher Barbara Landcart supplements her somewhat meagre income by writing love stories for magazines and managed to sell one a month for the first five months of this year. Can you work out the title of the story she sold in each month, which magazine bought it and how much they paid?

Clues

1 In April, Barbara found a buyer for her novelette called *The Orchid*. *Point Of View* was sold in the first quarter of the year.

2 The story sold in February brought Barbara just £100.

3 *Daydream* was published in *Lovebirds* magazine.

4 *Street Scene* was purchased for £160 the month after Barbara made a sale to *Cupid*.

5 The editor of *Soulmates* paid Barbara £140 for one of her stories.

6 *Loving Couples* magazine, which bought a story from Barbara in May, paid her less than £150.

	Month	Story	Magazine	Fee paid

Puzzle No 73

Game On

Several English villages still keep alive the strange old games dating back centuries. Can you work out which village plays which game and identify the two items needed to play it?

Clues

1 No village shares an initial letter with its game; and neither a village nor game has the same initial letter as the first word of either item used in the game.

2 Neither the milk churn nor the ham bone is used in the game at Oddleigh; this game isn't fryle turling, which doesn't involve either the bunch of feathers or the shepherd's crook.

3 Doodle knocking doesn't call for the use of either the horseshoe or the wooden stool, which aren't linked, nor is either of these items used in the game at Backwater.

4 Brole casting is the long-established game at Laffiton; it doesn't use any part of an animal's body, nor is any such part associated with the milk churn.

5 The turnip is linked with the bow and arrow, but neither in the village of Playwick nor in the game of stile haggling.

6 The game which features the bunch of feathers doesn't also feature the bucket; neither of these items plays a part in doodle knocking or throle clogging.

	Brole casting	Doodle knocking	Fryle turling	Stile haggling	Throle clogging	Bunch of feathers	Ham bone	Horseshoe	Pig's bladder	Turnip	Bow and arrow	Bucket	Milk churn	Shepherd's crook	Wooden stool
Backwater															
Laffiton															
Oddleigh															
Playwick															
Strangeham															
Bow and arrow															
Bucket															
Milk churn															
Shepherd's crook															
Wooden stool															
Bunch of feathers															
Ham bone															
Horseshoe															
Pig's bladder															
Turnip															

Village	Game	First item	Second item

Puzzle No 74

Les Chattaway

Each afternoon on our local radio station, Les Chattaway has various guests from around the county to talk about this and that. For example, below are details of this afternoon's show – from the information given, can you discover what time each guest is scheduled for, the subject that each will talk about with Les and the number of minutes allocated?

Clues

1 The first guest follows the news at 3.05pm and has been allocated the shortest time. The first guest isn't Dr John Hobbs, who will feature in the regular weekly health slot.

2 The 3.20pm guest isn't Kathleen Miller, who will be talking with Les for the longest period of time.

3 A man is on at 3.40pm to talk about his newly published book of poems; he hasn't been allotted twelve minutes.

4 The local history enthusiast isn't the guest just after the four o'clock news. The man talking at 4.35pm won't be doing so for exactly twelve minutes.

5 Arthur Shelton hasn't been allocated ten minutes.

6 Exactly eleven minutes will be filled by the guest talking about his or her toy collection; it isn't Jane Neville.

	Dr John Hobbs	Kathleen Miller	Jane Neville	Gordon Palmer	Arthur Shelton	Book of poems	Health	Local history	Toy collection	Work overseas	8 minutes	10 minutes	11 minutes	12 minutes	14 minutes
3.05															
3.20															
3.40															
4.05															
4.35															
8 minutes															
10 minutes															
11 minutes															
12 minutes															
14 minutes															
Book of poems															
Health															
Local history															
Toy collection															
Work overseas															

Time	Guest	Subject	No of minutes

Puzzle No 75

Blewbludd Court

Blewbludd Court is a tiny close tucked away in the City of London, occupied by six shops catering only to the very top people. Can you fill in on the plan the name of each shop and the trade carried on there?

Names: Catesby & Doone; Foxley & Glossin; Halkett & Jocelyn; Launce & Manders; Prior & Quarles; Rudiger & Scales
Businesses: Barber; bookseller; gunsmith; pharmacy; shoemaker; wine merchant

Clues

1 The barber's shop is numbered more than one lower than that of the wine merchant.

2 The gunsmith (specialising in handmade custom shotguns for grouse-shooting) isn't at number 6.

3 One of the original partners whose names still adorn the sign above number 2, the 'shoemakers to the gentry', although they've both been dead over a century, had a six-letter surname.

4 Catesby & Doone is at number 5 Blewbludd Court.

5 Foxley & Glossin's shop isn't numbered two lower than that of Halkett & Jocelyn, which isn't the bookseller.

6 The pharmacy is directly opposite Prior & Quarles, who aren't at number 1 or number 4.

7 The bookshop bears a number two lower than that of Rudiger & Scales' shop, which isn't the wine merchant's or the barber's.

1	3	5

Blewbludd Court

2	4	6

Shop No	Name	Business

Shop No	Name	Business

Starting tip:
Work out which trade is plied by Rudiger & Scales, then the position of that shop.

Puzzle No 76

Telecops 1

Albion TV's new summer schedules include five detective series imported from the USA. Can you work out each central character's surname, which is also the title of the series, that character's forename and occupation and the town or city where he or she is based?

Clues

1 *Blackwood* isn't set in Memphis, Tennessee.

2 Scott does his detective work in the frigid environment of Anchorage, Alaska.

3 The Chicago-based detective is surnamed Zitkin.

4 One of the series features the Chief of Police in the little town of Brewerton, Maine.

5 Nick is the security chief for a big industrial corporation.

6 Ben's surname is one letter shorter than that of the detective based in Las Vegas, who doesn't feature in *Torricelli*.

7 FBI agent McClintock isn't Pete.

8 Annie Gahagan isn't a private eye.

Series title	Forename	Occupation	Location

Puzzle No 77

Telecops II

Each of the TV detectives mentioned in the previous problem has been provided by the studio scriptwriters with a particular marital status, a background interest and an eccentricity of behaviour. From the clues given below and your answers to the previous problem, can you work out the details for each of the telecops?

Clues

1 The detective whose spouse died in a car accident and who is bringing up a young son alone relaxes by playing chess; this series isn't based in Brewerton, Maine.

2 In every episode of one series, the character whose hobby is computers tries and fails to give up smoking.

3 The FBI agent who devotes much spare time to running a youth club for underprivileged kids isn't the one who, separated from a still much-loved spouse, is constantly seeking self-improvement through correspondence courses; the latter doesn't feature in *Blackwood*.

4 The Detective Lieutenant isn't the telecop who's always reading British whodunnits in the classic 'body in the library' tradition.

5 The central character of *Zitkin* is still getting over a very messy divorce.

6 The forename of the superstitious detective who is always buying new lucky charms – who isn't the one whose spouse is confined to a wheelchair by a spinal problem – appears in the alphabetical list immediately ahead of that of the one who suffers from acrophobia.

7 A running joke in *Torricelli* concerns the central character's lack of ability as a cook.

First name	Marital status	Interest	Eccentricity

Puzzle No 78

Every One a Winner

The diagram shows a group of six allotments in the small town of Growell. Each is rented out to a different gardener and each of the six won first prize for a different vegetable at the recent Horticultural Show. Can you fully identify the owner of each of the allotments numbered 1 to 6 and say which vegetable was his speciality?

Clues

1 Tom's beetroots grow on an even-numbered allotment, which isn't next to that of Percy, whose surname isn't Plant.

2 The peas are produced on the allotment immediately right, as you look at the plan, of the one which grows the prize turnips.

3 As you enter through the gate and walk along the perimeter path, you come to Patch's allotment next after John's and next before that of the gardener who grows the prize leeks.

4 The allotment which produces the prize cauliflowers, which is adjacent to Tilth's, bears a number twice that of the one worked by Eddie Greenfinger.

5 Allotment 1 is rented by Mr Sprouting.

6 The potatoes aren't grown on any of the first three allotments, one of which belongs to Wilf.

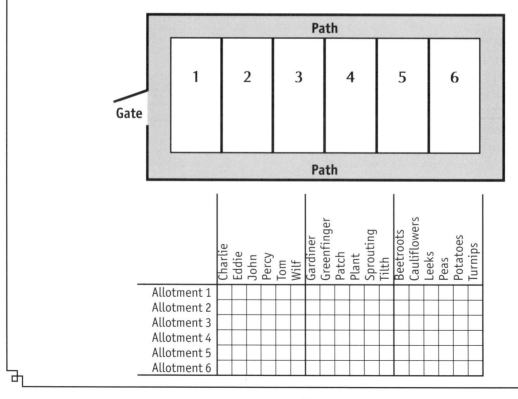

Puzzle No 79

Words of Wisdom

Though visits by his great-nephews to Great-Uncle Joe usually obliged them to listen to lengthy narratives about his exploits, on their last visit he invited them to do the talking and to explain certain modern terms of which he was ignorant. Can you work out where each boy sat, his age, the term which he was called upon to explain and the order in which the boys spoke?

Boys: Darren; Jack; Ron; Sean
Ages: 10; 11; 12; 13
Terms: CD-ROM; cyberspace; internet; sound bite

Clues
1 No boy gave his explanation in the alphabetical order of his place, eg boy A didn't speak first, etc.
2 The boy of 13 sat next to and left of Sean: the one who explained 'internet' was further right than either of these two.
3 The boy of 10 gave his definition next after Darren, who was more than one place to his left. The boy of 11 had his turn next before the one of 12.
4 The boy who spoke fourth is a year older than the one who spoke third.
5 Ron sat next left to the boy who volunteered to go first. The one who explained 'sound bite' was next to and right of the one who explained 'cyberspace'.
6 The definition of 'CD-ROM' wasn't given by the boy who sat at place C.

Boy	Name	Age	Term	Order

Starting tip:

Work out which boy sat at D and then when the 10-year-old spoke.

Puzzle No 80

The Wisdom of Sophocles

The fortunes of Oldfort United AFC were at a low ebb when they were taken over by a shipping billionaire I Sophocles just before the start of the new season. The first thing he did was to sack and replace five of the leading lights who had guided the side to relegation. Can you match the men sacked with their posts and their replacements and say in what order the new appointments were announced via the local media?

Clues

1 Al Spottam, the new youth organiser, was the next new face to be brought in after Dick Lining's replacement as team manager.

2 The third post to undergo a change of personnel was that of club secretary; the incumbent wasn't Luke Down, who wasn't the man replaced by Phil Lipp.

3 The new chief coach was appointed some time before the man who replaced Perry Luss.

4 A Paul Ling was replaced by Bobby Knupp.

5 Kenny Liftham was the fifth new name to be divulged to the local media.

6 The second man to be replaced was Mal Function.

The grid has the following column headings: Chief coach, Club secretary, Physiotherapist, Team manager, Youth organiser, Al Spottam, Benny Fitt, Bobby Knupp, Kenny Liftham, Phil Lipp, First, Second, Third, Fourth, Fifth.

The grid has the following row headings: A Paul Ling, Dick Lining, Luke Down, Mal Function, Perry Luss, First, Second, Third, Fourth, Fifth, Al Spottam, Benny Fitt, Bobby Knupp, Kenny Liftham, Phil Lipp.

Man sacked	Job	Replacement	Order

Puzzle No 81

Bob's Jobs

When Bob reached retirement age, he took up part-time work as a jobbing gardener at five of the large houses on the outskirts of the village. Can you work out on which day Bob worked at each of the five houses, name the latters' owners and say what line of business each is in?

Clues

1 Each week Bob looks after the garden of Mr Gross the stockbroker two days after tending the one at West Winds.

2 The garage owner's house is called Ten Gables.

3 The garden at Pinewood is tended by Bob earlier in the week than the caravan manufacturer's.

4 On Mondays, Bob works at Highfield, but he doesn't work for Mr Short on Tuesdays.

5 Mr Little makes use of Bob's gardening skills every Friday.

6 Bob isn't to be found in the garden of Greenlea on a Thursday.

7 The novelist employs Bob later in the week than Mr Longman.

	Greenlea	Highfield	Pinewood	Ten Gables	West Winds	Mr Burley	Mr Gross	Mr Little	Mr Longman	Mr Short	Airline pilot	Caravan manufacturer	Garage owner	Novelist	Stockbroker
Monday															
Tuesday															
Wednesday															
Thursday															
Friday															
Airline pilot															
Caravan manuf'r															
Garage owner															
Novelist															
Stockbroker															
Mr Burley															
Mr Gross															
Mr Little															
Mr Longman															
Mr Short															

Day	House	Owner	Occupation

Puzzle No 82

The Paragon in Character

Charles Lieteris' vigilante adventure hero, the Paragon, alias Peter Galahad, often assumed character rôles with bizarre names in his crusades against crooks beyond the reach of the law. For instance, in *The Paragon Hits Back* (1935), Galahad assumed five different disguises in the course of bringing a killer to justice. Can you work out each one's full name and occupation and the accent with which he spoke?

Clues

1 When posing as Barnaby, the Paragon used a shorter surname than when playing the rôle of Tobias, which wasn't the one for which he adopted a Bristolian accent.

2 The Paragon didn't call himself Pinchbeck when pretending to be a deck-hand from the coaster SS Daffodil.

3 In the character of a small-time bookmaker surnamed Skimpole, the Paragon tricked the killer's accomplice into giving away vital information, while posing as the Manchester-accented Zebedee gave him the chance to gain possession of the murder weapon, a pneumatic dart-gun.

4 Peter Galahad used the forename Jesse when pretending to be a taxi-driver.

5 As Alljack, the Paragon used a broad Liverpudlian accent; Uploft's accent wasn't Mancunian.

6 In chapter nine of the book, the Paragon transforms himself from a gardener with a Newcastle accent into Egbert Jellyby, while hiding from the villain's henchmen in a glamorous actress' dressing room.

Forename	Surname	Occupation	Accent

Puzzle No 83

Game, Set and Match

Tom Binman, a rising young tennis star, recently won a five-round tournament. Can you fully identify the opponent beaten in each round and say how the winning matchpoint was obtained in each match?

Clues

1 Tom was delighted to clinch his victory in the final in the grand manner, with a service ace.

2 Dennison, Tom's third-round opponent, didn't present him with his winning point.

3 The drop-shot winner put an end to the match in the round before Tom met Paul.

4 The volley was netted by Tom's next opponent after Tarquin and the one before Gavin Rankin.

5 Wayne wasn't Tom's opponent in the second round and Hurst didn't play him in the semi-final.

6 It was Thorpe, whose first name isn't Michael, who was beaten by one of Tom's passing shots to end their match.

	Gavin	Michael	Paul	Tarquin	Wayne	Dennison	Hurst	Rankin	Thorpe	Wilby	Ace serve	Drop-shot	Opponent double-faulted	Opponent netted volley	Passing shot
First round															
Second round															
Third round															
Semi-final															
Final															
Ace serve															
Drop-shot															
Opp double-faulted															
Opp netted volley															
Passing shot															
Dennison															
Hurst															
Rankin															
Thorpe															
Wilby															

Round	First name	Surname	Ending

Puzzle No 84

The First Millennium

It's not realised that Millennium projects were all the rage a thousand years ago at the end of the first Millennium in 1000 AD. In the village of Muddenhoe the elders had formed a committee to consider various schemes. Can you discover what Millennium monument each member suggested, its proposed location and estimated cost in silver pieces?

Clues

1 Oswin's Millennium project was to cost more than the cow-byre and the Manor Farm proposals added together; neither his nor Hubert's proposal was the one near the church that was to cost 220 silver pieces and Hubert's wasn't the cheapest.

2 Oswin's project was to cost more than Wat's South Field Millennium development.

3 The cost of Egbert's suggestion was an odd number of silver pieces and was greater than the cost of the Millennium Granary.

4 The cow-byre wasn't planned for the Abbey, while the bridge was to be built across the river.

5 The granary wasn't the 65-silver-piece project, while the pig-sty wasn't the most costly proposal.

6 Wilfred put forward plans for a Millennium duck-pond.

	Cow-byre	Duck-pond	Granary	Pig-sty	Stone bridge	Abbey	Church	Manor Farm	River	South Field	20 silver pieces	65 silver pieces	170 silver pieces	220 silver pieces	335 silver pieces
Egbert															
Hubert															
Oswin															
Wat															
Wilfred															
20															
65															
170															
220															
335															
Abbey															
Church															
Manor Farm															
River															
South Field															

Member	Project	Location	Cost

Turn of the Centurion

Only five centurions of the XXth legion were resident at their base in Deva at the time of the Governor's visit, the rest being engaged in ultra-mural operational duties. The centurions, with their centuries were drawn up in numerical order for inspection. Can you work out the name of each centurion and the colour and device on each banner?

Centurions: Billius; Brutus; Decibillius; Raucus; Stentorius
Colours: Blue; green; red; white; yellow
Devices: Bear; hawk; leopard; lion; serpent

Clues

1 The century under Brutus (known to his men as Ate Two), whose device wasn't the serpent, stood next in front of the one with the green banner and next behind the one whose device was the lion.

2 The century with the white banner was lined up in front of the one whose commander was Billius (Sillius Billius to his troops).

3 The banner of century III was blue; the one with the hawk device was one place in front of the one with the yellow banner.

4 The century with the red banner was more than one place behind the one under Raucus; the Governor, who started at the front, inspected the century with the serpent device some time before the one commanded by Stentorius.

5 Decibillius wasn't the first or last in line; the leopard wasn't the device of century V; and the serpent wasn't the device of century IV.

Centurion	Name	Colour	Device

Starting tip:

Work out the colours of centuries I and II.

Puzzle No 86

Kicking the Habit

Five friends are inveterate cigarette smokers. Each has vowed to give up the weed; indeed, each has done so on a different number of occasions, only to start up again. Can you match the names with the number of cigarettes each smokes on average every day, say how many times each has tried and failed to give up smoking and discover the longest period of abstinence each has achieved?

Clues

1 The smoker who managed to last out the longest has already tried to give up on five occasions.

2 The person who once managed to go 10 days without lighting up, who isn't Ben, smokes an average of 30 a day.

3 Maggie isn't the woman who smokes 35 cigarettes a day.

4 Lesley, who has the largest daily consumption of the five, has given up on one fewer occasion than Joy.

5 The 20-a-day smoker has never contrived to go longer than 6 days on the occasions when he or she has tried to stop, which number two fewer than the total attempted by the person whose longest period without a smoke is 12 days.

6 The person who has given up four times, whose longest period without a cigarette isn't 8 days, smokes an average of 10 cigarettes a day more than Charles.

	20 a day	25 a day	30 a day	35 a day	40 a day	4 times	5 times	6 times	7 times	8 times	6 days	8 days	10 days	12 days	14 days
Ben															
Charles															
Joy															
Lesley															
Maggie															
6 days															
8 days															
10 days															
12 days															
14 days															
4 times															
5 times															
6 times															
7 times															
8 times															

Name	Daily total	No of attempts	Longest period

Snakes and Ladders

Five friends are playing snakes and ladders, throwing the dice in the alphabetical order of their names. On one particular turn each landed on either a snake or a ladder. Can you discover the dice throw of each, whether they landed on a snake or a ladder and the beginning and ending square numbers of each turn?

Clues

1 Brian threw first, got an even number on the dice and moved from square 65, but didn't end on 49; Ellen threw a lower number than the person who ended in the lead, who hadn't thrown a 6.

2 The player who threw a 3 moved immediately after the person who started on square 73 and immediately before the person who ended on 21.

3 The player who reached square 21 threw an odd number on the dice.

4 A throw of 5 and either a snake or a ladder brought one of the players to square 35; it was neither Martin nor Wendy.

5 Wendy wasn't on square 12 and neither she nor the player on square 12 threw a 1.

6 One player took a snake from 84 to 53.

	Throw					Start					Finish				
	1	3	4	5	6	6	12	65	73	84	21	35	49	53	89
Brian															
Dave															
Ellen															
Martin															
Wendy															
21															
35															
49															
53															
89															
6															
12															
65															
73															
84															

Player	Throw	Start	Finish

Puzzle No 88

Safe…

Five trusted members of the staff of a firm dealing in highly sensitive matters had individual safes, to which only they had the six-digit combination. Can you work out the first three digits of each man's combination, all of which consisted of different combinations of the digits 0 to 4 inclusive?

Clues

1 No digit occurs more than once in any man's combination and each appears just once in each position.
2 To gain access to his safe Trustey has to begin by dialling a zero.

3 Neither Wise nor Loyell has a 3 in his combination of numbers.
4 Parfitt's first digit is two higher than his third digit.
5 The man whose first digit is a 2 doesn't follow it with a 3 when he goes to open his safe.
6 The third digit Sphinx has to dial is two lower than the second digit of Wise's combination; the latter's three digits read in ascending order, though they aren't consecutive.
7 Trustey's second digit is higher than Sphinx's first.

Name	First digit	Second digit	Third digit

Puzzle No 89

...keeping

Similarly, the last three digits of each man's combination consisted of different combinations of the digits 5 to 9 inclusive. From the clues given below, plus the information obtained by solving the problem on the facing page, can you work out all the details?

Clues

1 As with the first three digits, each of the final three occur once in each position and none is repeated in any man's combination.

2 The man whose first digit is a 1 has a 6 as his fourth digit; his final digit is higher than Parfitt's.

3 The digit formed by adding Parfitt's first two digits together doesn't appear in his full combination, nor in that of the man whose third digit is a 3.

4 Loyell's fourth digit is the same as the fifth digit of the man whose third digit is a 2.

5 The man whose second digit is a 3 doesn't have 5 as his fifth digit.

6 Eight is the fifth digit of the man whose first digit is one lower than that of the man whose second digit is 0.

7 Trustey's fourth digit is two higher than Sphinx's fifth.

8 The combination whose fourth digit is 9 doesn't end in a 5.

	Fourth					Fifth					Sixth				
	5	6	7	8	9	5	6	7	8	9	5	6	7	8	9
Loyell															
Parfitt															
Sphinx															
Trustey															
Wise															
SIXTH 5															
6															
7															
8															
9															
5															
6															
7															
8															
9															

Name	Fourth digit	Fifth digit	Sixth digit

Puzzle No 90

Claycaster Museums

Although Claycaster is only a small town, it's one of the oldest in England and boasts no less than five museums, though none is housed in purpose-built premises. Can you work out the original use of each museum building, its address and the name of its curator?

Clues

1 The Clayshire Regiment Museum, which has Colonel A C Quire as its curator, isn't the one housed in a converted Victorian mansion in Iveagh Square.

2 Mr S E Cure isn't in charge of the museum situated in St Bride's Green.

3 Ms O B Tain is curator of the museum housed in what used to be a wholesale grocer's warehouse, while Dr G Ather is in charge of the one in Wallace Street. The latter (which isn't the building that used to be the County Courthouse) hasn't the name of the town in its title.

4 The Social History Museum is in Geffrye Lane, in the oldest part of the town; the Claycaster Art Museum, of which Mr H Oard isn't the curator, occupies the former fire station.

	Church	Courthouse	Fire station	Mansion	Warehouse	Geffrye Lane	Horniman Street	Iveagh Square	St Bride's Green	Wallace Street	A C Quire	G Ather	H Oard	O B Tain	S E Cure
Claycaster M															
Claycaster Art M															
Clayshire Regt M															
Nat History M															
Social History M															
A C Quire															
G Ather															
H Oard															
O B Tain															
S E Cure															
Geffrye Lane															
Horniman Street															
Iveagh Square															
St Bride's Green															
Wallace Street															

Museum	Building	Address	Curator

Puzzle No 91

Hope Springs Eternal

Five football fans, whose teams had met with varied fortunes last season, were each looking forward, as such optimists invariably do, to the start of the new one. Can you identify the five and say which team each man supports and work out how each team fared last season?

Clues

1 The Midchester City supporter, who isn't Pitch, is convinced his team will recover from last season's relegation and regain their rightful place in a higher division.

2 The Swanfield United fan's surname is Turnstyle.

3 Padbury Rovers, who aren't supported by Tim, aren't the team who just missed out on promotion by losing in the play-offs.

4 Simon's side avoided relegation by the narrowest of margins, by winning their last match of the campaign.

5 Willie is a Grayburn Athletic supporter; he isn't Flagg, whose team occupied a mid-table berth at the end of last season, having never threatened to go either up or down.

6 Carl Stand's team are still in the same division as they were last year.

	Barrier	Flagg	Pitch	Stand	Turnstyle	Grayburn Athletic	Ludford Town	Midchester City	Padbury Rovers	Swanfield United	Just avoided relegation	Just missed promotion	Mid-table	Promoted	Relegated
Bernie															
Carl															
Simon															
Tim															
Willie															
Just avoided rel'n															
Just missed pro'n															
Mid-table															
Promoted															
Relegated															
Grayburn Athletic															
Ludford Town															
Midchester City															
Padbury Rovers															
Swanfield United															

Forename	Surname	Team	Fate last season

Puzzle No 92

On Site

A builder employs five men, each of whom has a distinctive hair feature and a different character trait. Can you work out each man's age and describe his hair feature and his trait?

Clues

1 Lance, who has long, dark hair and Bob, who never stops telling jokes, are both in their thirties.

2 The man who whistles while working isn't as old as Darren.

3 The man with the shaven head, who isn't 28, is noted for asking the foreman silly questions.

4 Sean isn't the man with red hair.

5 The fair-haired man is 33.

6 Robin, who isn't the man aged 37, is older than both the man with the short, dark hair and the one whose conversation consists entirely of football chat.

	22	28	31	33	37	Fair hair	Long, dark hair	Red hair	Shaven head	Short, dark hair	Asks silly questions	Sings	Talks football	Tells jokes	Whistles
Bob															
Darren															
Lance															
Robin															
Sean															
Asks silly questions															
Sings															
Talks football															
Tells jokes															
Whistles															
Fair hair															
Long, dark hair															
Red hair															
Shaven head															
Short, dark hair															

Name	Age	Hair	Trait

Puzzle No 93

Order Papers

Bundles of copies of tonight's *Evening Mail* and *Evening News* are being unloaded from the distributor's delivery van. From the following poem, can you discover the address of each named shop and how many copies of each paper its proprietor ordered?

Clues

Clark, the station bookstall, didn't order 40 *Mail*;
The newsagent in Carlton Street has 40 *News* for sale.
Thirty *Mails* were on the van for Pargetter's to sell;
They have more copies of the *News* than are for Maidenwell.

The shop in Gladstone Square had 60 *Mails* on the van,
And 20 more of *Evening News* than went to Silverman.
One shop ordered 50 *Mails* and 30 of the *News*;
This wasn't the newsagent with the shop in Abbey Mews.

The 20 *Mails* and 20 *News* went off to
    different places.
The largest order for the *News* didn't go off
    to Lacey's.
We don't know what Melville's had, so
    there we'll have to stop;
Can you work out the quantities of papers
    at each shop?

	Abbey Mews	Carlton Street	Gladstone Square	Maidenwell	Railway station	Mail 20	30	40	50	60	News 10	20	30	40	50
Clark															
Lacey															
Melville															
Pargetter															
Silverman															
NEWS 10															
20															
30															
40															
50															
MAIL 20															
30															
40															
50															
60															

Newsagent	Address	Evening Mail	Evening News

Puzzle No 94

Things That Go Bump...

Mistmere Manor has the reputation of being the most haunted house in the country. Can you work out what noise, if any, each of five of its apparitions makes, where in the Manor it manifests itself and to what century the spook belongs?

Clues

1 An eerie silence is associated with the poltergeist, which belongs to the century after that of the apparition which haunts the main bedroom.

2 The screams do not emanate from either of the ghosts or the 14th-century apparition.

3 The apparition which appears in the hall belongs to one century later than the one to which the banshee belongs, but more than one earlier than that of the spook which groans; this one is always seen inside, unlike either the screamer or the 14th-century apparition.

4 Neither the male ghost nor the one which is sighted on the rooftop utters shrieks; both of these apparitions belong to later centuries than that of the one which whistles, which isn't the kelpie, which belongs to two centuries earlier than the apparition which haunts the drawing room.

5 The apparition which appears on the terrace belongs to one century before that of the one which shrieks.

Apparition	Noise	Haunt	Century

Stagecoach

The Wilgo Farr stagecoach travels along the bare, lonely Kansas highway, its twelve passengers disposed as shown, all longing to reach the next stop. All have different names, no-one having a first name with the same initial as their surname. Those on top all face forwards, those inside face each other. A window-seat is any seat except seats 5, 2, 11 and 8.

George sits directly below Blake and Craski directly below Jake. Tom isn't facing forwards. John's seat-number is 4 less than Simon's. Chris has a window-seat as does Pete. Janssen and Hennessy are immediately next to each other, the latter having the higher-numbered window-seat. Trent is between Les and Halliday, while Colin is directly below Victor. Luce's seat-number is 5 higher than that of Verney, while Parker is on top.

Stone sits directly opposite Rackham, while Gudgeon has an even seat-number directly above Tom. The seat-numbers of Luce and Hennessy total the same as those of Roger and Jake. The surnames of those in seats 10 and 11 contain 5 letters and one of the passengers is called Hank.

Can you identify and locate each man, writing his name into his respective seat?

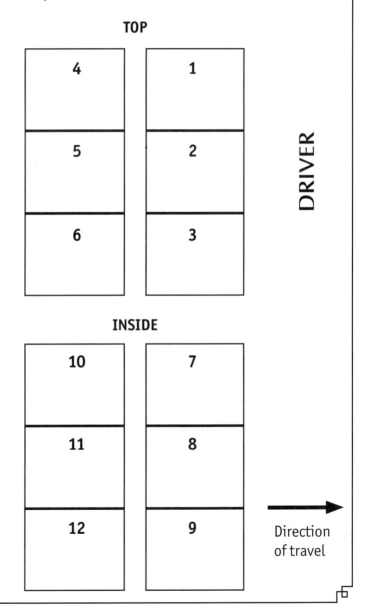

TOP

4	1
5	2
6	3

DRIVER

INSIDE

10	7
11	8
12	9

Direction of travel

Puzzle No 96

Seek and Ye Shall Find

Six members of a metal-detectors' club were given permission by a farmer to use their instruments in one of his fields. Each member was allocated a different one of the six strips lettered A to F in the plan and each found one object, in the positions marked by a cross. Can you fully identify the member given each strip and describe the item he or she found?

Clues

1 The position in which Digger found the Roman coin is nearer the bottom of the field than the one in which Stella was disappointed to turn up a bottle top in an adjacent strip.

2 The six-inch nail registered on the metal detector being wielded by the person in strip A.

3 Tanya Hunt was working in the next strip to the person who found the ring.

4 The rusty washer was unearthed in the strip immediately next to the one in which the sixpence was detected, neither of these objects being found by Mr Quest.

5 Bleep was working in the strip next to and right of that in which you would find Search as you look at the plan.

6 Strip E was allocated to Roy, who didn't unearth a coin, but Josie wasn't allocated strip D.

7 Michael's strip was nearer to the gate of the field than Seeking's.

8 One of the male metal detectors was allocated strip B.

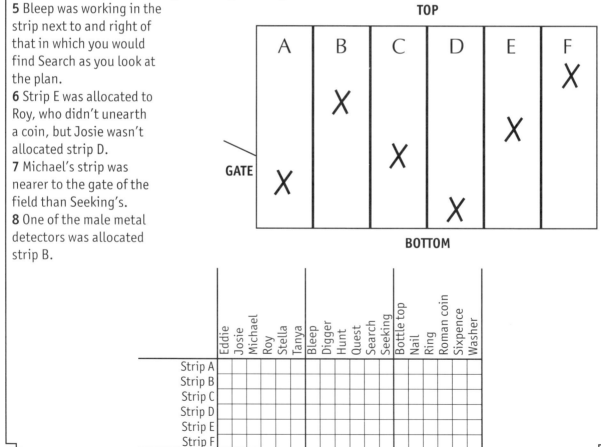

Puzzle No 97

Pandemonium Properties

The growth of population in Pandemonium had led to an acute housing shortage and when Performance Chariots Plc wanted to increase their workforce, they decided to build some houses adjoining the factory. Can you work out the name, age and occupation of the tenant of each house?

Tenants: Dexterus; Nitidus; Radius; Rotundus; Industrius
Ages: 22; 28; 32; 34; 40
Occupations: Bookkeeper; joiner; painter; security guard; wheelwright

Clues
1 Dexterus' house was next right to that of the bookkeeper, who was more than six years older.
2 The house occupied by the 28-year-old was further to the left than those of both Industrius and the security guard, neither of whom was the youngest of the five.
3 Neither the painter, who wasn't Radius, nor the tenants on either side of him, was 40.
4 The tenant of No 1 was six years younger than the tenant of No 5.
5 Nitidus lived next left to the wheelwright, who was older, though not next oldest.
6 The combined ages of Rotundus and the joiner equalled those of Radius and the tenant of No 4.

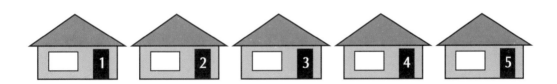

House No	Tenant	Age	Occupation

Starting tip:

Work out the occupations of the men aged 28 and 22.

- 99 -

Puzzle No 98

On the Oche

Four men were taking part in the first round of an international darts competition. Can you fully identify each player, say which country he represented, work out his age, how many maximum scores of 180 he achieved in his first-round match and name the wife or girlfriend in the audience cheering him on?

Clues

1 Willie, the Scotsman, is two years older than Ruth's boyfriend, whose surname is Double.

2 The man aged 29 registered a total of twelve maximum scores of 180 during his first round match.

3 Jenny was shouting on the player who scored 180 eleven times.

4 Gloria's husband is the English player, who scored one more maximum than Nick, who is older than the man surnamed Board.

5 Gail's husband is 31 years of age.

6 Mr Flight, the American player, scored an odd number of 180s.

7 Tony is the oldest of the four competitors.

8 Cliff shares a surname initial with another of the players.

	Board	Bull	Double	Flight	England	Scotland	USA	Wales	27	29	31	33	10	11	12	13	Gail	Gloria	Jenny	Ruth
Cliff																				
Nick																					
Tony																					
Willie																					

Forename	Surname	Country	Age	Maximums	Supporter

Puzzle No 99

Guardians of the Gates

The Dome is the closely-guarded residence of the ruler of the planet Rogon. It can only be approached via four gates, each guarded by a slave from a different subject race conquered by the Rogons. Each guard is armed with the weapon appropriate to his native planet. Can you name the guard on each of gates 1 to 4, say which conquered planet he is from and identify his weapon?

Guards: Glun; Lurgan; Tribb; Zabec
Planets: Blunk; Dozar; Nuglon; Quarg
Weapons: Axe; grenades; laser gun; poison darts

Clues

1 Quarg is the most civilised of the planets conquered by the Rogons and the guard from there is equipped with a laser gun; he guards the gate next clockwise from the one guarded by Tribb.

2 Lurgan is on duty at gate 2, while the guard from Nuglon isn't at gate 3.

3 Glun is the guard with the poison darts; the gate he guards has a number higher than that manned by the guard from Blunk.

4 The guard on gate 4, who isn't Zabec, is armed only with an axe, but he can wield it to devastating effect.

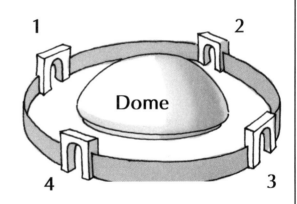

Gate	Guard	Planet	Weapon

Starting tip:

First work out the number of the gate guarded by Glun.

- 101 -

Military Mutts

Four Army dog-handlers have just completed training with their new dogs and received postings to military bases in different parts of Britain. Can you work out the name and colour of each soldier's German Shepherd dog and say where the partnership is being sent? In the grid, ranks are listed in ascending order.

Clues

1 Lance-Corporal Griffon and his dog will be going to Colchester, a garrison town since Roman times.

2 Kerry is a cream-coloured, long-haired German Shepherd bitch.

3 Arrow's handler has a six-letter surname and so does Demon's; the latter pair are being sent to guard the SAS base at Hereford.

4 Corporal Talbot's dog is black and tan; the all-black dog isn't Private Basset's.

5 The man being sent to Edinburgh ranks immediately above Scout's handler.

	Arrow	Demon	Kerry	Scout	Black	Black and tan	Cream	Grey	Aldershot	Colchester	Edinburgh	Hereford
Private Basset												
Lance-Corp Griffon												
Corporal Talbot												
Sergeant Whippet												
Aldershot												
Colchester												
Edinburgh												
Hereford												
Black												
Black and tan												
Cream												
Grey												

Handler	Dog's name	Dog's colour	Posting

Puzzle No 101

Faraway Places

Sir Eustace Faraway was one of the great explorers of the late 19th Century and on each of his four major expeditions he gave his name to a newly-discovered landscape feature. Can you work out where each of the dated expeditions went, who accompanied Sir Eustace and what he named in his own honour?

Clues

1 The South American expedition (which began in an earlier month of the year than the one on which Mount Faraway received its name) resulted in the discovery of the beautiful Faraway Falls.

2 Sir Eustace's companion on the expedition which began in March 1887 was a very distinguished Army officer.

3 On his first expedition, which took him to West Africa, Sir Eustace was accompanied by neither Major Malvern nor Professor Mendip, the latter of whom was with him when he discovered the Faraway Gorge.

4 The expedition to Australia didn't set out in January 1889.

5 It was in July 1884 that Sir Eustace and Dr Cheviot set out together.

	Australia	Central Africa	South America	West Africa	Dr Cheviot	Colonel Lennox	Major Malvern	Professor Mendip	Gorge	Lake	Mountain	Waterfall
March 1882												
July 1884												
March 1887												
January 1889												
Gorge									
Lake									
Mountain									
Waterfall									
Dr Cheviot					
Colonel Lennox					
Major Malvern					
Professor Mendip					

Date	Destination	Companion	Named feature

Lookalikes

The Daily Lantern, a popular tabloid, has been holding a competition to find readers who look like celebrities. Below are some details of the four winning women; can you work out each one's full name and occupation and say who she looks like?

Clues

1 The housewife's surname isn't Adams.

2 The surname of the woman who resembles actress and comedienne Maureen Lipman is listed alphabetically between those of Iris and the traffic warden, who isn't Ms Baker.

3 Jane looks amazingly like American singer Dolly Parton.

4 Kate is Ms Clark.

5 The waitress who looks like actress Jane Fonda isn't Lucy; the latter's surname alphabetically precedes the former's.

	Adams	Baker	Clark	Dixon	Housewife	Nurse	Traffic warden	Waitress	Dolly Parton	Jane Fonda	Marilyn Monroe	Maureen Lipman
Iris												
Jane												
Kate												
Lucy												
Dolly Parton												
Jane Fonda												
Marilyn Monroe												
Maureen Lipman												
Housewife												
Nurse												
Traffic warden												
Waitress												

Forename	Surname	Occupation	Lookalike

Puzzle No 103

Ghost Storeys

Ghastleigh Castle has four Towers, each with a haunted room. From the clues below, can you discover the name of each Tower and its haunted room and identify the ghost that frequently manifests itself there?

Towers: Black Tower; Drogo's Tower; New Tower; Sorcerer's Tower
Rooms: King's Chamber; Sorcerer's Den; Treasure Room; Whistling Room
Ghosts: Brother Luke; Lady Edith; Lord Ivo; Old Meg

Clues
1 The King's Chamber (Charles II spent a night there, hiding from The Roundheads) is in tower C.
2 The Sorcerer's Den is, unsurprisingly, in the Sorcerer's Tower, which is the next in alphabetical order after the New Tower (built in 1340) where Lady Edith's ghost haunts the scene of her murder.
3 The Whistling Room (the sound comes from the badly-built chimney, not the resident phantom) isn't in Drogo's Tower, named after the original builder of the castle.
4 Brother Luke appears in the tower marked A on the plan; Tower B isn't haunted by Lord Ivo and isn't the location of the Treasure Room, where the Ghastleigh family silver is still stored.

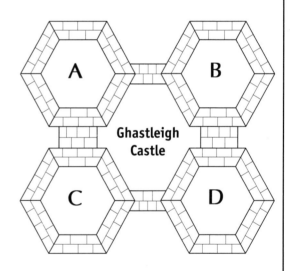

Ghastleigh Castle

Tower	Name	Room	Ghost

Starting tip:
Work out the position of the Sorcerer's Tower.

Solutions

Puzzle No 1 Birthday Boy
Jacob's grandma sent the teddy-bear card (clue 1). The person from Crewe who sent the card with the cat design isn't Aunt Laura (clue 2), so Laura's card featured rabbits and Jacob's godmother is from Crewe. Esme lives in Oxford (clue 3), so Rachel is from Crewe and Laura lives in Tavistock.

In summary:
Cat, Rachel, godmother, Crewe.
Rabbits, Laura, aunt, Tavistock.
Teddy-bear, Esme, grandma, Oxford.

Puzzle No 2 Sun Seekers
The Greens live at No 6 (clue 4), so the Browns are at No 10 (clue 1) and the Smiths at No 8. The Browns went to Lanzarote (clue 1). The Smiths went in June (clue 2), so the Greens went to the Algarve in July (clue 3), the Smiths went to Cyprus and the Browns went in May.

In summary:
Brown, No 10, Lanzarote, May.
Green, No 6, Algarve, July.
Smith, No 8, Cyprus, June.

Puzzle No 3 Circumfailures
The Vesta's crewperson wasn't Kay Kidd (clue 2), Larry Lafitte (clue 4) or Mike Morgan (clue 5), so Tom Teach. The crewperson of the Clansman which travelled 16 miles (clue 1) wasn't Kay Kidd (clue 2), Tom Teach (clue 3) or Mick Morgan (who went two miles further, clue 5), so Larry Lafitte and (clue 4) the Katinka sprang a leak. Kay Kidd's swamped yacht (clue 2) was the Shrimp. Mick Morgan captained the Katinka and went 20 miles (clue 5) and the Vesta went 18 miles. By elimination, the Shrimp went 14 miles. The Vesta hit a rock (clue 3) and the Clansman's rudder broke.

In summary:
Clansman, Larry Lafitte, 16 miles, rudder broke.
Katinka, Mick Morgan, 20 miles, sprang leak.
Shrimp, Kay Kidd, 14 miles, swamped.
Vesta, Tom Teach, 18 miles, hit rock.

Puzzle No 4 Lots of Strangeness
Lot 2 sold for £600 (clue 3). Lot 1 wasn't the crundle-fan (clue 1), the Mukkinese battle-horn (clue 2) or the nose-flute (clue 4), so the whelk-scraper. The £800 lot wasn't the battle-horn (clue 2), whelk-scraper or nose-flute (clue 4), so the crundle-fan. It wasn't lot 4 (clue 2), so lot 3 and (clue 1), lot 2 was Calathumpian. By elimination, the Mukkinese battle-horn was lot 4 and lot 2 was the nose-flute. The Anjinian artefact was sold for £800 (clue 4). Thus lot 1 went for £700. By elimination, the whelk-scraper was Prytesmic and the battle-horn sold for £500.

In summary:
Lot 1, Prytesmic, whelk-scraper, £700.
Lot 2, Calathumpian, nose-flute, £600.
Lot 3, Anjinian, crundle-fan, £800.
Lot 4, Mukkinese, battle-horn, £500.

Puzzle No 5 Managing a Break
The person surnamed King is Colin (clue 4) and Beth is mountaineering (clue 3). Robbins who is yachting isn't Dawn (clue 4), so Alan. Alan is the personnel manager (clue 1) and Colin is ballooning. The scuba-diving production manager (clue 2) is Dawn, so Beth is Spencer and Dawn is Lane. Beth is the sales manager (clue 4), so Colin is in accounts.

In summary:
Alan Robbins, personnel, yachting.
Beth Spencer, sales, mountaineering.
Colin King, accounts, ballooning.
Dawn Lane, production, scuba-diving.

Puzzle No 6 Step Down Here!
Contestant number 3 was from York (clue 4) and Dawn was contestant number 5 (clue 6). The first contestant's estimate was £175 (clue 2). Leonard was called down next after the woman from Gravesend whose guess was £180 (clue 1), so Leonard was third and (clue 1) the woman from Gravesend was second. Martina was from Esher (clue 3), so Agatha was from Gravesend. Martina wasn't the first contestant (clue 3), so the fourth and the first was Richard. He wasn't from Filey (clue 2), so Taunton and Dawn was from Filey. Leonard's guess was £200 (clue 3) and Martina's £150, so Dawn's was £210. Leonard was exactly right (clue 5).

In summary:
1, Richard, Taunton, £175.
2, Agatha, Gravesend, £180.
3, Leonard, York, £200 (correct value).
4, Martina, Esher, £150.
5, Dawn, Filey, £210.

Puzzle No 7 Filmyflabbies
Dum rides on his skateboard (clue 1) and the purple Filmyflabby carries a shopping-bag. KooKoo is blue and hasn't a pogo-stick or umbrella (clue 4), so wellies and her shape is thus a diamond (clue 5). The yellow Filmyflabby bears a circle (clue 5). The pink one isn't identified by a triangle or star (clue 3), so a square. GaGa has a square (clue 6) but not the umbrella (clue 3), so the pogo-stick. The purple Filmyflabby isn't Potti (clue 1), so Loco; thus Potti has the umbrella. Loco's shape isn't a star (clue 2) or circle (clue 5), so a triangle. Potti's isn't a star (clue 2), so a circle and Dum is green and has a star.

In summary:
Dum, green, skateboard, star.
GaGa, pink, pogo-stick, square.
KooKoo, blue, wellies, diamond.
Loco, purple, shopping-bag, triangle.
Potti, yellow, umbrella, circle.

Puzzle No 8 Late Starters
The electrician was late on Wednesday (clue 3) and the Tuesday latecomer had overslept (clue 6). The joiner whose car wouldn't start (clue 5) was late on Monday and Winston

is the electrician. Trevor's reason for being late on Thursday was a transport problem (clue 1). The man whose wife was ill wasn't late on Friday (clue 2), so Wednesday and he's Winston, thus Trevor is the plumber. Trevor's excuse wasn't that he'd run out of petrol (clue 2), so that he'd missed the bus and it was on Friday that a workmate ran out of petrol. This wasn't the bricklayer (clue 4), so the plasterer and the bricklayer overslept. Leslie wasn't late on Tuesday or Friday (clue 6), so Monday. The bricklayer isn't Karl (clue 4), so Ryan and Karl is the plasterer.

In summary:
Karl, plasterer, Friday, ran out of petrol.
Leslie, joiner, Monday, car wouldn't start.
Ryan, bricklayer, Tuesday, overslept.
Trevor, plumber, Thursday, missed bus.
Winston, electrician, Wednesday, wife ill.

Puzzle No 9 Spy Stories

Mark Newcombe is posing as a salesman (clue 5) and Gerald Howard is K12 (clue 7). X27 posing as a journalist isn't Andrew Brooke (clue 3). X27 isn't Dorothy Elton (clue 2), so Jane Kavanagh, alias Kelly Locke (clue 4). The agent posing as an engineer isn't X15 (clue 2), so the engineer is from K section and Dorothy is G34 and (clue 6) is posing as Chris Dixon. The fake naturalist's name is Pat Quinlan (clue 7), so Dorothy Elton is posing as a tourist. Gerald Howard isn't posing as a naturalist (clue 7), so an engineer and Andrew Brooke is posing as Pat Quinlan. Mark Newcombe isn't posing as Jean Kervin (clue 5), so Sandy Tyler and Gerald Howard is posing as Jean Kervin. Mark Newcombe isn't K20 (clue 1), so X15 and K20 is Andrew Brooke.

In summary:
Andrew Brooke, K20, Pat Quinlan, naturalist.
Dorothy Elton, G34, Chris Dixon, tourist.
Gerald Howard, K12, Jean Kervin, engineer.
Jane Kavanagh, X27, Kelly Locke, journalist.
Mark Newcombe, X15, Sandy Tyler, salesman.

Puzzle No 10 Stone Age Sport

The first bout was the hog-weight contest (clue 1), Thugg was in the fourth (clue 4) and Agg was in the third (clue 5). Egg and Slugg were thus in the fifth (clue 6) and the mammoth-weight contest in the fourth. Igg fought at sabre-tooth-tiger-weight (clue 2), thus was in the second bout. Hugg was the mouse-weight wrestler (clue 3), so Slugg and Egg were jackal-weights. By elimination, Hugg was in the third bout. Jugg wasn't in the first (clue 1), so second and Lugg was in the first. Thugg's opponent wasn't Ogg (clue 4), so Ugg and Ogg fought Lugg.

In summary:
Agg, Hugg, mouse-weight, third.
Egg, Slugg, jackal-weight, fifth.
Igg, Jugg, sabre-tooth-tiger-weight, second.
Ogg, Lugg, hog-weight, first.
Ugg, Thugg, mammoth-weight, fourth.

Puzzle No 11 In the Picture

Photo F is of Grant (clue 4) and C is of Gallery (clue 7). Roger's isn't H (clue 5), so C (clue 1), Dee Claim is in B and Hammett in A. Queue is in D (clue 2) and Patricia in E. By elimination, Pitt's photo is on the right-hand wall, so (clue 3) Lavinia's is G and Pitt's H. Lynes's photo is also on the right-hand wall, so (clue 6) Marshall's is H and Lynes's F. Stage is in E (clue 7), so Prompt in G. Queue is Nancy (clue 2) and Edgar is Hammett.

In summary:

A, Edgar Hammett.	B, Dee Claim.
C, Roger Gallery.	D, Nancy Queue.
E, Patricia Stage.	F, Grant Lynes.
G, Lavinia Prompt.	H, Marshall Pitt.

Puzzle No 12 To Market, to Market...

The farmer who sold ducks bought grain (line 15). The one who sold goats didn't buy meal or straw (lines 7-8), nor is he McTavish who bought the plough (lines 3-4), so he bought a gun. One cow was sold (line 2). The farmer who bought straw sold two animals but not sheep (lines 9-10), so he was Higgins selling pigs (line 1). Farmer Moore had three to sell (line 12). Webster didn't sell four or five (line 11), so one and (by elimination) Webster bought meal and McTavish sold five sheep. There weren't four goats (lines 5-6), so three and there were four ducks.

In summary:
Higgins, two pigs, straw.
Hodgson, four ducks, grain.
McTavish, five sheep, plough.
Moore, three goats, gun.
Webster, one cow, meal.

Puzzle No 13 Safety Factor

The factor 15 brand was £8.50 (clue 1). Yvonne's factor 2 wasn't £5.00 or £7.00 (clue 2) or £6.50 (clue 6), so £4.75. Yvonne bought Taneezee (clue 5) and the factor 4 was £7.00 and was Bronzetone (clue 4). Edward bought factor 4 (clue 6), Michelle bought factor 8 and the factor 6 was £6.50. By elimination, factor 8 was £5.00. It wasn't Safe-Sun (clue 6) and Oliver used Supersol (clue 7), so Michelle bought Tropique and Chloe used Safe-Sun. The latter wasn't factor 6 (clue 3), so factor 15 and Supersol was factor 6.

In summary:
Chloe, Safe-Sun, factor 15, £8.50.
Edward, Bronzetone, factor 4, £7.00.
Michelle, Tropique, factor 8, £5.00.
Oliver, Supersol, factor 6, £6.50.
Yvonne, Taneezee, factor 2, £4.75.

Puzzle No 14 Sam's Samples

Wicks' product arrived on the 8th (clue 3) and the talcum powder on the 4th (clue 7), so (clue 1) McCavitys' toothpaste came on the 7th. Ogdens' sample came in July (clue 5). The firm whose product came on 25th November (clue 6) wasn't Pollards' (clue 7), so Bryants'. Pollards' didn't come on the 4th

Solutions

(clue 7), so the 15th and Ogdens' on the 4th. Pollards' didn't come in May (clue 2), so March and the soap powder came in May. Bryants' product wasn't shampoo (clue 4), so coffee; thus Pollards sent the shampoo and Wicks soap powder came on the 8th.

In summary:

March 15th, shampoo, Pollards.
May 8th, soap powder, Wicks.
July 4th, cosmetics, Ogdens.
September 7th, toothpaste, McCavitys.
November 25th, coffee, Bryants.

Puzzle No 15 Where There is Discord...

Christine's favourite is Ryan (clue 5). Janet is the secretary (clue 2). The membership secretary who favours Stefan isn't Melanie Tone-Deff (clue 6), or Selma (clue 1), so Trudy. The chairperson's surname is Harsh (clue 4). Janet's surname isn't Jangle or Jarring (clue 1), so Rawcuss and her favourite is thus Bongo (clue 7). Harsh isn't Selma (clue 4), so Christine. Miss Jangle's favourite isn't Jake (clue 1) or Dirk (clue 3), so Stefan. By elimination, Selma's surname is Jarring, thus she's the press officer (clue 2) and Melanie is the treasurer. Selma's favourite is Dirk (clue 1), so Melanie's is Jake.

In summary:

Christine Harsh, chairperson, Ryan.
Janet Rawcuss, secretary, Bongo.
Melanie Tone-Deff, treasurer, Jake.
Selma Jarring, press officer, Dirk.
Trudy Jangle, membership secretary, Stefan.

Puzzle No 16 Summer Jigsaw

The word in box 11 has an even number of letters (clue 2), SOLSTICE is in box 7 (clue 5) and the words in boxes 5 and 9 are of the same length (clue 6), so (clue 1) LAST is in box 5, WEIGHT in box 1 and HOUSE in box 6. TERM is in the same vertical column as SCHOOL (clue 3). The word in box 9 has four letters (clue 6) and isn't FETE or WINE (clue 4), so TIME. HOLIDAY is in box 10 (clue 7) and INDIAN in box 11. SCHOOL is the longest word remaining to be placed, so isn't in box 8 (clue 8), thus (clue 3) it is in box 4. FETE is in box 3 (clue 4) and WINE in box 2. MID is in box 8 (clue 8) and TERM in box 12.

In summary:

1, WEIGHT.	2, WINE.	3, FETE.
4, SCHOOL.	5, LAST.	6, HOUSE.
7, SOLSTICE.	8, MID.	9, TIME.
10, HOLIDAY.	11, INDIAN.	12, TERM.

Puzzle No 17 Freshers' Fancy

The wine-tasting society meeting with 30 members wasn't on Tuesday (clue 1), nor had Tuesday's meeting 6 or 10 members (clue 2). Emma's French film society didn't have 6 (clue 2) and David's had 10 (clue 4), so there were at least 15 at Emma's meeting. Thus Tuesday's had 21 (clue 2) and there were 15 at the French films meeting. Tuesday's meeting wasn't of the astronomy society (clue 1) or sailing club (clue 2), so the play-

reading group and (clue 4) David's was on Thursday. David's wasn't the astronomy society (clue 1), so the sailing club and 6 attended the astronomy club. Kate's Wednesday meeting didn't attract 30 (clue 3), so 6. The wine-tasting society met on Friday (clue 1) and the French films club on Monday. John attended Tuesday's meeting (clue 5) and Ian was a member of the wine-tasting group.

In summary:

David, sailing, Thursday, 10.
Emma, French films, Monday, 15.
Ian, wine-tasting, Friday, 30.
John, play-reading, Tuesday, 21.
Kate, astronomy, Wednesday, 6.

Puzzle No 18 Arms and the Man

Since the pink elephant is on the top row (clue1), the dragon is in quarter 4 (clue 4) and the blue creature in quarter 3. The von Plonka creature is black (clue 2). The lion representing the Muddelkopf alliance isn't orange (clue 3), so blue. The elephant isn't in quarter 1 (clue 1), so quarter 2 and the dragon is from the Klotzky arms. By elimination, the eagle is in quarter 1 and is black, so the elephant is from the Nitwitz family and the dragon is orange.

In summary:

1, eagle, black, von Plonka.
2, elephant, pink, Nitwitz.
3, lion, blue, Muddelkopf.
4, dragon, orange, Klotzky.

Puzzle No 19 Waking Moments

The man in room 401 requested an alarm call at 7.15 (clue 5). The 6.15 call wasn't for room 112, 104 (clue 3) or 208 (clue 4), so 316 and thus was requested by Mr Bryant (clue 6), who also asked that his suit be pressed (clue 3). The guest who ordered breakfast in his room requested a call at 6.30 (clue 4) and room 208 booked the 7.00 call. The man who ordered breakfast wasn't in room 112 (clue 3), so 104. Mr Harvey who requested the 6.45 call (clue 1) was thus in room 112. His other request wasn't for a taxi (clue 3) or a late supper, as that was Mr Price (clue 1), so it was the checking of train times. Mr Henderson's room number wasn't 104 (clue 2), so he asked for the 7.00 call and Mr Price the 7.15 call. By elimination, Mr Spencer was in room 104 and Mr Henderson wanted the taxi.

In summary:

Mr Bryant, 316, 6.15, press suit.
Mr Harvey, 112, 6.45, check train times.
Mr Henderson, 208, 7.00, order taxi.
Mr Price, 401, 7.15, late supper in room.
Mr Spencer, 104, 6.30, breakfast in room.

Puzzle No 20 Tor Tour

Camworthy Tor is approached from the north-east (clue 3) and the 940-foot tor from the north-west (clue 4). The 890-foot Highpound Tor isn't approached from the east (clue 6) or south-east (higher than the fifth, clue 2), so from the

Solutions

south-west and it's thus the fourth (clue 4). The second tor is Binaton (clue 5). The third is 1,840 feet (clue 2). The fifth isn't Pavey (clue 1) or Camworthy (clue 3), so Chagley. It isn't 1,130 feet (clue 1) or 1,560 feet (clue 5), so 940 feet. Binaton isn't 1,560 feet (clue 5), so 1,130 feet. The first tor isn't Pavey (clue 1), so Camworthy and Pavey is third. The tor approached from the south-east is Binaton (clue 2) and Pavey is approached from the east.

In summary:
First, NE, Camworthy Tor, 1,560 feet.
Second, SE, Binaton Tor, 1,130 feet.
Third, E, Pavey Tor, 1,840 feet.
Fourth, SW, Highpound Tor, 890 feet.
Fifth, NW, Chagley Tor, 940 feet.

Puzzle No 21 You Have Been Selected...

Friday's letter didn't offer £12,000 (clue 3), £10,000 (clue 4), £9,000 (clue 5) or £13,000 (clue 6), so £8,000. It wasn't signed by Lavinia Glenn (clue 1), Alison Meadows (clue 2), Caroline Dale (clue 4) or Katy Campion (clue 6), so Melanie Vaill. The prize offered by the gardening firm was more than £10,000 but not £13,000 (clue 2), so £12,000 and Alison Meadows offered £13,000. Monday's letter wasn't from Lavinia Glenn (clue 1), Alison Meadows (clue 2) or Caroline Dale (clue 4), so Katy Campion. The health products letter didn't offer £8,000, thus £9,000 and wasn't offered by Lavinia Glenn (clue 1) or Katy Campion (clue 6), so Caroline Dale. Thursday's and Friday's letters weren't for health products (clue 1), clothing or gardening (clue 5). Thursday's didn't offer £10,000 (clue 4) or £9,000 (clue 5), so £13,000. Thus Friday's was for books (clue 3), Thursday's for household goods and Wednesday's for gardening products. Tuesday's was for health products (clue 1), so Monday's was for clothing and offered £10,000.

In summary:
Monday, clothing, Katy Campion, £10,000.
Tuesday, health items, Caroline Dale, £9,000.
Wednesday, gardening items, Lavinia Glenn, £12,000.
Thursday, household goods, Alison Meadows, £13,000.
Friday, books, Melanie Vaill, £8,000.

Puzzle No 22 Dynasty

The father isn't Cranko or Binko (clue 1), Plonko (clue 2) or Bonko (clue 3), so Grunko. His wife's name with a 'u' (clue 4) isn't Flunka (clue 2), so Bunka. The fourth son isn't Cranko (clue 1), Plonko (clue 2) or Bonko (clue 3), so Binko whose wife (clue 4) is thus Flunka. Plonko is the third son (clue 2). The eldest isn't Cranko (clue 1), so Bonko and Cranko is the second. Twinka is Plonko's wife (clue 1). Cranko's wife isn't Clinka (clue 1), so Blinka and Bonko's is Clinka.

In summary:
Father: Grunko, m. Bunka.
First son: Bonko, m. Clinka.
Second son: Cranko, m. Blinka.
Third son: Plonko, m. Twinka.
Fourth son: Binko, m. Flunka.

Puzzle No 23 Robotixcops

The Howard is going to Sahara City (clue 3) and male robots are going to Adelbourne and Ulan Bator (clues 2 and 4). The female crossing patrol robot is going to Southbrit (clue 3) and isn't the Thelma (clue 1), so the Daphne and the Thelma is going to New York. The Martin isn't going to Ulan Bator (clue 4), so Adelbourne and the Arnold to Ulan Bator. The Martin isn't the 4804 (clue 1), 2317 or 4801 (clue 4), so the 3695. The Howard isn't the 4801 (clue 1), so 2317 and the 4801 is the Arnold. The Howard isn't the speed cop (clue 2), administrator (clue 3) or beat cop (clue 4), so the traffic warden. Thus the Arnold is the speed cop (clue 2) and the Martin is the administrator. The beat cop is the Thelma and is model 4804 (clue 4), so the Daphne is model 3762.

In summary:
Arnold, 4801, speed cop, Ulan Bator.
Daphne, 3762, crossing patrol, Southbrit.
Howard, 2317, traffic warden, Sahara City.
Martin, 3695, administrator, Adelbourne.
Thelma, 4804, beat officer, New York.

Puzzle No 24 Tasting the Tipple

Max Tipler chose St Michel (clue 1) and the Chateau Dufay is a Burgundy (clue 3). Lena Barr chose Cabernet Sauvignon which isn't the Abbe Phillipe (clue 6), or Neuchamps (clue 5), so is the Baron Claude sold by Waitway. Tesrose's wine is Neauchamps (clue 5). Asco's wasn't chosen by Max Tipler or Ivor Cork (clue 2) or Phil Glass (clue 3), so Jilly Van Blonck. It isn't the Chateau Dufay (clue 3), so the Abbe Phillipe. The Burgundy wasn't chosen by Phil Glass (clue 3), so Ivor Cork and Phil Glass chose Neuchamps. Co-fields' wine wasn't chosen by Max Tipler (clue 4), so Ivor Cork and Max Tipler chose Gatebury's. The Chablis isn't the St Michel or Neuchamps (clue 1), so Abbe Phillipe. The Beaujolais is the St Michel (clue 5) and Neuchamps is the Entre-Deux-Mers.

In summary:
Abbe Phillipe, Chablis, Jilly Van Blonck, Asco.
Baron Claude, Cabernet Sauvignon, Lena Barr, Waitway.
Chateau Dufay, Burgundy, Ivor Cork, Co-fields.
Neuchamps, Entre-Deux-Mers, Phil Glass, Tesrose.
St Michel, Beaujolais, Max Tipler, Gatebury.

Puzzle No 25 Off the Rails

The Titanic was in a collision (clue 6) and the Lusitania's brakes failed (clue 7). The locomotive which exploded due to a burst boiler wasn't the Mary Celeste (clue 3) or the Waratah which was wrecked on Friday (clue 1), so the Hesperus. The Mary Celeste was wrecked on Thursday (clue 3) and Monday's incident involved overturning in the road (clue 5). The Hesperus didn't crash on Tuesday (clue 1), so Wednesday and (clue 2) the Mary Celeste's connecting-rod failed. By elimination, the Lusitania's incident was on Monday and the Titanic's on Tuesday. The Titanic's regulator jammed (clue 4), so the Waratah's valve-gear failed and it ran through the buffers. The Mary Celeste fell into the river.

Solutions

In summary:
Monday, Lusitania, overturned in road, brakes failed.
Tuesday, Titanic, collision, regulator jammed.
Wednesday, Hesperus, explosion, boiler burst.
Thursday, Mary Celeste, fell into river, connecting-rod broke.
Friday, Waratah, ran through buffers, valve gear failed.

Puzzle No 26 Cactus Creek

Saloon A belonged to Miss Nelly Rogers (clue 4). Poker was played in C (clue 3). Frenchie Leroy's attraction was roulette and wasn't D (clue 2), so was B. The Lone Star had the lowest prices and didn't belong to Miss Nelly Rogers or Joe Doolan (clue 5), so Tom Bowden. By elimination it was D, C was Joe Doolan's and A offered the stage show. C was the Gold Nugget (clue 1). B wasn't the Wagon Wheel (clue 2), so the Thunderbird and A was the Wagon Wheel.

In summary:
A, Wagon Wheel, Miss Nelly Rogers, stage show.
B, Thunderbird, Frenchie Leroy, roulette.
C, Gold Nugget, Joe Doolan, poker.
D, Lone Star, Tom Bowden, lowest prices.

Puzzle No 27 True Stories

Martin is in page 8's story (clue 1). Phil is in 'She stole my husband' (clue 4). The story about Jon is later in the magazine than 'I can't stop cheating' (clue 3), so page 5's 'I married my brother-in-law' which doesn't involve Greg (clue 1), features Bob and (clue 6) is Jean's. Karen's is on page 14 (clue 2), so Annie's is on page 17 and 'I can't forget him' is on page 20. 'He won't talk to me' by Beverley (clue 5) is thus on page 8. Jon isn't in 'I can't stop cheating' (clue 3), so 'I can't forget him' and Greg is in 'I can't stop cheating'. Karen's features Greg (clue 2) and Annie's is 'She stole my husband', so Carol wrote 'I can't forget him'.

In summary:
Page 5, 'I married my brother-in-law', Jean, Bob.
Page 8, 'He won't talk to me', Beverley, Martin.
Page 14, 'I can't stop cheating', Karen, Greg.
Page 17, 'She stole my husband', Annie, Phil.
Page 20, 'I can't forget him', Carol, Jon.

Puzzle No 28 Love's Luvvies

The magician's assistant is Wescott (clue 5) and the country singer is at the Grand Theatre (clue 6). Miss Stevens is at one of the clubs and isn't the juggler or Alma the impressionist (clue 4), so she's the chorus girl. Alma is also at a club (clue 4). Miss Wescott isn't at the Pavilion Theatre (clue 5), so the Marine Theatre, thus she's Marion and the juggler is at the Pavilion. She isn't Fiona (clue 2) or Pam (clue 3), so Julie. Pam's surname is McLaverty (clue 1), so she's at the Grand Theatre and the chorus girl is Fiona. Fiona isn't at Manfred's (clue 2), so the Regency and Alma is at Manfred's. Alma's surname is Newbold (clue 1) and Julie's is Pegram.

In summary:
Alma Newbold, impressionist, Manfred's Club.
Fiona Stevens, chorus girl, Regency Club.
Julie Pegram, juggler, Pavilion Theatre.
Marion Wescott, magician's assistant, Marine Theatre.
Pam McLaverty, country singer, Grand Theatre.

Puzzle No 29 In the Area

The tea tent is in area C (clue 1) and Lucy is in charge of D (clue 6), so Ronnie's darts competition is in B and (clue 3) Sheila is running area A. Jackson is looking after area F (clue 2). Janet Foster isn't in area C (clue 1), so E. Sheila's surname is Benson (clue 5) and she'll be in charge of welly-throwing, so Ronnie's surname is Pearson. Lucy's isn't Walters (clue 6), so Horner and Walters is in charge of the tea tent. The fortune-teller's tent is in either D or E (clue 4) and the football competition is in either E or F. Since one of these two activities is in E, the pet show is in either D or F, thus (clue 6) it's in F. Lucy Horner is the fortune-teller (clue 4) and the football competition is being run by Janet Foster. Madge's surname isn't Jackson (clue 6), so Walters and Charles's is Jackson.

In summary:
A, welly-throwing, Sheila Benson.
B, darts, Ronnie Pearson.
C, tea tent, Madge Walters.
D, fortune-teller, Lucy Horner.
E, football, Janet Foster.
F, pet show, Charles Jackson.

Puzzle No 30 On the Run

Dermot was runner 4 (clue 1) and the person in green was second (clue 4). Hill was thus first (clue 2) and Craig second. Warren Radley was third (clue 3) and Alan's surname is Hill. Warren wasn't in blue (clue 3), so red and Dermot wore blue. Craig's surname is Marchant (clue 4) and Dermot's is Lowther.

In summary:
1, Alan Hill, yellow.
2, Craig Marchant, green.
3, Warren Radley, red.
4, Dermot Lowther, blue.

Puzzle No 31 Nicked!

The surname of the armed robber begins with S (clue 7), but isn't Skinner (clue 5) or Smart (clue 6), so Sharp. His nickname isn't Corky (clue 1), Flash (clue 3), Knocker (clue 4) or Shifty (clue 7), so Tip. Tip was arrested by Corner (clue 2). Hunter caught an arsonist (clue 1). The man who arrested the forger isn't Grabham (clue 4) or Trackman (clue 5), so Catchmore. The nickname of the forger isn't Flash (clue 3), Knocker (clue 4) or Corky (clue 5), so Shifty. His surname doesn't begin with S (clue 7) and isn't Wiley (clue 3), so Twist. Corky's surname isn't Smart (clue 1) or Skinner (clue

5), so Wiley. His offence wasn't burglary (clue 7) but he stole something (clue 5), thus a car. The man arrested by Trackman also stole (clue 5), thus he's the burglar. His surname isn't Skinner thus isn't Knocker (clue 5), so he's Flash and his surname is Smart. By elimination, Skinner is Knocker. He wasn't arrested by Grabham (clue 4), so Hunter. Thus Shifty was arrested by Catchmore and Grabham caught the car thief.

In summary:
DI Catchmore, Shifty Twist, forgery.
DI Corner, Tip Sharp, armed robbery.
DI Grabham, Corky Wiley, car theft.
DI Hunter, Knocker Skinner, arson.
DI Trackman, Flash Smart, burglary.

Puzzle No 32 Duel Personality

The Monday duel wasn't over the card game (clue 1), an actress (clue 3), spilled wine (clue 4) or the play (clue 5), so the personal insult. The man who insulted Sir Rawnsley wasn't Sir Guy Glaive (clue 1), the Comte de Falchion or Sir Toby Tuck (clue 2) or Lord Claymore (clue 6), so the Hon Hugh Hanger. Lord Claymore didn't quarrel over the play or the card game (clue 6) and a knight spilt the wine (clue 4), so Lord Claymore clashed with Rawnsley over the actress. The Comte de Falchion was wounded in the left shoulder (clue 2), so the man who was wounded in the left arm (clue 3) was the Hon Hugh Hanger. Friday's duellist wasn't Sir Guy (clue 1), the Comte (clue 2) or Lord Claymore (clue 3), so Sir Toby Tuck. So the Comte fought on Thursday (clue 2) and Wednesday's duel ended with a right leg wound. Lord Claymore fought on Wednesday (clue 6) and the duel over the play was on Tuesday, thus (by elimination) involved Sir Guy Glaive. The knight wounded in the right arm after spilling wine (clue 4) was thus Sir Toby Tuck. By elimination, Sir Guy Glaive was wounded in the right shoulder and the Comte de Falchion argued over the card game.

In summary:
Monday, Hon. Hugh Hanger, personal insult, left arm.
Tuesday, Sir Guy Glaive, play, right shoulder.
Wednesday, Lord Claymore, actress, right leg.
Thursday, Comte de Falchion, card game, left shoulder.
Friday, Sir Toby Tuck, spilled wine, right arm.

Puzzle No 33 Out of Class

Joan is from Bristol (clue 3), the dermatology student is from Lincoln (clue 4) and a woman is from Coventry (clue 6), so Dan who is studying geriatrics (clue 5) is from Guildford. Graham the rugby player isn't from Lincoln (clue 4), so Manchester. The conservationist is from Coventry (clue 6). The embryology student belongs to the Chess Club (clue 1), so is from Bristol. The Drama Society member isn't Dan (clue 5), so is from Lincoln and Dan is a member of the Arts Club. The neurology student isn't from Coventry (clue 6), so Manchester and the Coventry student is a trainee pathologist. She isn't Marie (clue 2), so Sarah and Marie is from Lincoln.

In summary:
Dan, Guildford, geriatrics, Arts Club.
Graham, Manchester, neurology, Rugby Team.
Joan, Bristol, embryology, Chess Club.
Marie, Lincoln, dermatology, Drama Society.
Sarah, Coventry, pathology, Conservation Group.

Puzzle No 34 The Inn Thing

The Hare and Hounds changed its name in February (intro). It isn't in Rye Street (clue 1), Malt Road (clue 3), Grape Lane (clue 4) or Hops Hill (clue 5), so Barley Square. The pub renamed in December isn't the Mermaid and Dolphin (clue 1), Elephant and Grasshopper (clue 3), Laughing Frog (clue 4) or Ticklish Trout (clue 5), so Pig and Platypus. It isn't in Malt Road (clue 3), Grape Lane (clue 4) or Hops Hill (clue 5), so Rye Street. It wasn't called the White Horse or Rose and Crown (clue 1) or the Black Bull (clue 2), so the Red Lion. September's name change wasn't to the Elephant and Grasshopper (clue 3), Laughing Frog (clue 4) or Ticklish Trout (clue 5), so the Mermaid and Dolphin. The Black Bull wasn't in Hops Hill (clue 2) or Malt Road (clue 3), so Grape Lane. The Ticklish Trout isn't in Grape Lane or Hops Hill (clue 2), so Malt Road. Its old name wasn't the White Horse or Black Bull (clue 3), so the Rose and Crown. The Ticklish Trout changed its name in April or July (clue 5) and the Hops Hill pub in July or September. Thus the Grape Lane pub didn't change in July nor the Laughing Frog in April (clue 4), so the pub which changed in April is the Ticklish Trout, the Hops Hill pub changed its name in July and the pub in Grape Lane in September. By elimination, the Laughing Frog changed its name in July and the Elephant and Grasshopper is the new name of the Hare and Hounds. The Laughing Frog was thus the White Horse. The Rose and Crown was renamed in April (clue 1), so the Black Bull in September.

In summary:
Black Bull, Mermaid and Dolphin, Grape Lane, September.
Hare and Hounds, Elephant and Grasshopper, Barley Square, February.
Red Lion, Pig and Platypus, Rye Street, December.
Rose and Crown, Ticklish Trout, Malt Road, April.
White Horse, Laughing Frog, Hops Hill, July.

Puzzle No 35 Mobile Menace

Thursday's call lasted 17 minutes (clue 4) and the 13-minute call was in the pub (clue 6), so Tuesday's call on the train (clue 1) lasted 26 minutes and the one from the wife lasted 2 minutes. The call from a companion's mother was taken on the park bench (clue 5), so that of 2 minutes was whilst in the shop queue. Friday's was from a girlfriend (clue 3). Tuesday's wasn't from the secretary (clue 1), so work colleague. The wife's call wasn't on Wednesday (clue 2), so Monday. Friday's lasted 13 minutes (clue 3), so Wednesday's lasted 7 minutes. Wednesday's call wasn't taken in the restaurant (clue 2), so on the park bench and Thursday's was in the restaurant and was from the secretary.

Solutions

In summary:
Monday, shop queue, 2 minutes, wife.
Tuesday, train, 26 minutes, work colleague.
Wednesday, park bench, 7 minutes, mother.
Thursday, restaurant, 17 minutes, secretary.
Friday, pub, 13 minutes, girlfriend.

Puzzle No 36 Elderleigh People
Henry died in 1902 (clue 1) and the subject of picture E died in 1908 (clue 3). So Edward in B died in 1896 (clue 4) and the sister in C died in 1899. The male general wasn't Edward or Samuel (clue 6), so Henry. The admiral is in D (clue 7), so he's Samuel and (clue 6) Henry is in F. Samuel didn't die in 1905 (clue 7), so 1911 and the subject of A died in 1905. Irene the nun isn't in A or E (clue 5), so C. The explorer wasn't Bertha or Edward (clue 2), so Hannah. She isn't in E (clue 3), so A. By elimination, Bertha is in E. The poetess (female) wasn't Edward, so Bertha. Edward was the painter.

In summary:
A, Hannah, explorer, 1905.
B, Edward, painter, 1896.
C, Irene, nun, 1899.
D, Samuel, Admiral, 1911.
E, Bertha, poetess, 1908.
F, Henry, General, 1902.

Puzzle No 37 Return of the Paragon
The story published in August 1934 has a forger as its villain (clue 1) and Against The Odds was published in February 1933 (clue 4). In Vienna features the blackmailer and wasn't published in 1935 (clue 3), so in June 1932. Baron Van Damm featured in the March 1935 story (clue 5). In New York featuring Max Gottfried wasn't published in 1934 (clue 1), so in November 1935. Dr Soong appeared in a title which included the name of a city but not Vienna (clue 3), so he was in In Cairo. Thus Baron Van Damm was in Strikes Again and In Cairo was about the forger. Against The Odds doesn't feature Igor Kagovitch (clue 4), so Princess Sonja. Thus the smuggler was in In New York (clue 2) and Igor Kagovitch is the blackmailer. Princess Sonja isn't a spy (clue 4), so she's the jewel thief and the spy is Baron Van Damm.

In summary:
...Against The Odds, Princess Sonja, jewel stealing, February 1933.
...In Cairo, Dr Soong, forging, August 1934.
...In New York, Max Gottfried, smuggling, November 1935.
...In Vienna, Igor Kagovitch, blackmail, June 1932.
...Strikes Again, Baron Van Damm, spying, March 1935.

Puzzle No 38 Aye-Aye?
The order ending in ...the binnacle was given in 1841 (clue 6), so (clue 3) the one ending in ...the yardarm was given in 1843, Hands... in the 1844 order and the captain bound for New York issued his confusing signal in 1845. The destination of the ship on which the 1844 signal was given wasn't Rio (clue 1), Cairo (clue 4) or Bombay (clue 5), so Panama. The order ending ...to diving stations wasn't given in 1842 or 1845 (clue 1), so 1844 and Keelhaul... in 1843. Abandon... didn't begin the signal in 1841 or 1842 (clue 4), so 1845. ...six bells didn't complete this signal (clue 4), so completed the 1842 signal. By elimination, the 1845 signal ended with ...the mainbrace. The order beginning Heave... thus ended with ...the binnacle (clue 5) and Bombay was the 1842 destination. Rio was the 1841 destination (clue 1) and Cairo the 1843 one. Splice... began the 1842 signal.

In summary:
1841, Rio, Heave the binnacle.
1842, Bombay, Splice six bells.
1843, Cairo, Keelhaul the yardarm.
1844, Panama, Hands to diving stations.
1845, New York, Abandon the mainbrace.

Puzzle No 39 Miss Raffles
Miss Raffles' May job wasn't as cook (clue 2), gardener's boy (clue 3), housemaid (clue 5) or governess (clue 6), so secretary. This job wasn't at Arnesdon Castle (clue 1), Tipsham House (clue 3), Ditchley Place (clue 4) or Lovell Hall (clue 6), so Fendon Abbey. The September job wasn't as cook (clue 2), gardener's boy (clue 3) or housemaid (clue 5), so governess. She worked at Lovell Hall in August (clue 6) and for the Duchess of Chalk in July. The owner of Fendon Abbey wasn't Lady Le Doux (clue 1), Lady Babbage (clue 3) or Sir Arnold Wilkey (clue 5), so Lord Shipton. Her employer in June wasn't Lady Babbage (clue 3) or Sir Arnold Wilkey who she worked for after being a housemaid (clue 5), so Lady Le Doux. Lady Le Doux's home wasn't Arnesdon Castle (clue 1) or Ditchley Place (clue 4), so Tipsham House. At Tipsham House she wasn't a cook (clue 2) or gardener's boy (clue 3), so housemaid. Thus (clue 4) Ditchley Place belonged to Lady Babbage who (by elimination) employed her in September. Thus she was at Arnesdon in July as a gardener's boy (clue 3) and Lovell Hall belonged to Sir Arnold Wilkey for whom she was a cook.

In summary:
May, Lord Shipton, Fendon Abbey, secretary.
June, Lady Le Doux, Tipsham House, housemaid.
July, Duchess of Chalk, Arnesdon Castle, gardener's boy.
August, Sir Arnold Wilkey, Lovell Hall, cook.
September, Lady Babbage, Ditchley Place, governess.

Puzzle No 40 Travelling Bags
Mr Flyer flew to Madrid (clue 5). The man who flew to Vienna wasn't Mr Jett, whose luggage went to Cairo (clue 1), so Mr Case. The person flying to New York whose luggage went to Nairobi wasn't Mrs Fare the wedding guest (clue 3), so Miss Ticket. The person at the business conference in Frankfurt (clue 6) was thus Mr Jett and Mrs Fare went to Rome. The one whose luggage went to Bombay wasn't Mrs Fare (clue 2) or Mr Flyer (clue 5), so Mr Case. He wasn't paying a family visit

Solutions

(clue 2) or taking a week's holiday (clue 7), so took a weekend break. The person who went on holiday wasn't Mr Flyer (clue 7), so Miss Ticket and Mr Flyer paid a family visit. Mrs Fare's luggage went to Venice (clue 4) and Mr Flyer's to Paris.

In summary:
Mr Case, Vienna, weekend break, Bombay.
Mrs Fare, Rome, attending wedding, Venice.
Mr Flyer, Madrid, family visit, Paris.
Mr Jett, Frankfurt, business conference, Cairo.
Miss Ticket, New York, holiday, Nairobi.

Puzzle No 41 All Aboard

There are 61 passengers on coach A (clue 4) and the Dutch tourists are on E (clue 6). The coach with 63 passengers isn't C, E or F (clue 1) or D (clue 3), so B. Alan drives C (clue 1) and the Americans are on D. The Indian party of 69 aren't on F (clue 5), so C. The 66 passengers aren't on D (clue 3) or E (clue 6), so F. Douglas drives E and hasn't 65 passengers (clue 6), so 67 and 65 are on D. Lewis drives A (clue 3). Desmond's Japanese passengers aren't on F (clue 2), so B. The ones on A aren't French (clue 4), so Austrian and the French are on F. Roger doesn't drive D (clue 5), so F. Carl drives D.

In summary:
A, Lewis, Austrian, 61.
B, Desmond, Japanese, 63.
C, Alan, Indian, 69.
D, Carl, American, 65.
E, Douglas, Dutch, 67.
F, Roger, French, 66.

Puzzle No 42 Ubiquitous Ursula

The 6.00 appearance wasn't on Computer Fun (clue 2), A Good Start or Give Us A Hint (clue 3), Hellidays (clue 4) or Value For Money (clue 5), so Winner Takes All. The (first) 12.30 appearance wasn't on Computer Fun (clue 2), A Good Start (clue 3), Hellidays (clue 4) or Value For Money (clue 5), so Give Us A Hint. The Channel 8 programme wasn't Winner Takes All (clue 1), A Good Start or Give Us A Hint (clue 3), Hellidays (clue 4) or Value For Money (clue 5), so Computer Fun. Its time wasn't 4.00 (clue 1), 2.30 or 3.00 (clue 3), so 5.30 and A Good Start was at 3.30. Winner Takes All was thus on Channel 7 (clue 1) and the 4.00 programme was on Channel 6. The Channel 1 programme wasn't A Good Start or Give Us A Hint (clue 3), so Value For Money. Thus A Good Start was on Channel 4 (clue 3) and Give Us A Hint on Channel 3. Value For Money was on Channel 1 (clue 5), so the 4.00 programme was Hellidays and Value for Money was at 2.00.

In summary:
12.30, Channel 3, Give Us A Hint.
2.00, Channel 1, Value For Money.
3.30, Channel 4, A Good Start.
4.00, Channel 6, Hellidays.
5.30, Channel 8, Computer Fun.
6.00, Channel 7, Winner Takes All.

Puzzle No 43 Cabbages and Kings?

The topic raised by man D wasn't modern youth (clue 2), the Health Service (clue 4) or pensions (clue 5), so television standards. The man who denounced modern youth is 80 or 82 (clue 2), as was the one who was critical of pensions (clue 5), so the two who spoke about the Health Service and television standards are 76 and 78. One of these is David (clue 2). so Norman is 78 or 80 (clue 1). The 82-year-old isn't Peter (clue 5), so Charles. The second speaker wasn't C or D (clue 6). Man D didn't speak first or fourth (clue 5), so and the pensions spokesman fourth. The latter is Norman (clue 1), aged 80 (clue 6) who (by elimination) is B. The first speaker isn't man A (clue 3), so C and man A spoke second, about the Health Service (clue 4). The critic of modern youth is 82 (clue 2) and David is 78. Modern youth was thus Charles's topic and Peter is man A, aged 76.

In summary:
A, Peter, 76, Health Service, second.
B, Norman, 80, pensions, fourth.
C, Charles, 82, modern youth, first.
D, David, 78, television standards, third.

Puzzle No 44 Bed and Breakfast

There were 80 guests at All Comers (clue 1) and Vince and Jenny ate sausages when 50 guests were present (clue 3). Thus (clue 6) there were 15 when they had baked beans and 30 when they stayed at Adcaster Mill. The second hostel visited was Old Hallows (clue 2). The third hostel had 65 guests (clue 4), thus wasn't Pembury Castle (clue 5), so Monckton Hall. The fifth night wasn't at All Comers (clue 1) or Pembury Castle (clue 5), so Adcaster Mill. Sausages were eaten at the first hostel visited (clue 3), so baked beans at the second. By elimination, All Comers was visited fourth and Pembury Castle first. The food at All Comers wasn't muesli (clue 1) or scrambled egg (clue 5), so cornflakes. Muesli was eaten at Adcaster Mill (clue 1), so scrambled egg at Monckton Hall.

In summary:
First, Pembury Castle, 50, sausages.
Second, Old Hallows, 15, baked beans.
Third, Monckton Hall, 65, scrambled egg.
Fourth, All Comers, 80, cornflakes.
Fifth, Adcaster Mill, 30, muesli.

Puzzle No 45 Wish We Weren't Here

Neither Thursday's nor Friday's cards were from John (clue 1), Mike or George (clue 5). Paula's card arrived on Thursday or Friday (clue 5), so (by elimination) her husband is Nigel or Garry. Since only one couple have names of equal length, Paula is one of that pairing who holidayed in England (clue 4). Neither Sarah nor Verna is married to Garry or Nigel (clues 2 and 4), thus neither woman's card arrived on Thursday or Friday. So Verna's came on Tuesday or Wednesday (clue 1), John's on Monday or Tuesday and that from Italy on Wednesday or Thursday. George's card, which wasn't from Scotland or Greece (clue 3) came on Monday or Tuesday (clue

Solutions

5), thus was from Spain. Bev didn't go to Spain, Scotland or Greece (clue 3), so Italy. Monday's card was from Spain (clue 3), Tuesday's from Scotland and Wednesday's from Greece; so that from Italy arrived on Thursday and the one from England on Friday. Mike's arrived on Wednesday (clue 5). Garry didn't go to Italy (clue 5), so he was with Paula, Nigel's wife is Bev, John's card came on Tuesday and Verna's on Wednesday. Alison didn't go to Spain (clue 4), so her husband is John and Sarah's is George.

In summary:
Monday, Sarah, George, Spain.
Tuesday, Alison, John, Scotland.
Wednesday, Verna, Mike, Greece.
Thursday, Bev, Nigel, Italy.
Friday, Paula, Garry, England.

Puzzle No 46 Happy Daze

Mon	Tue	Wed	Thur	Fri	Sat	Sun
	R	E	W	M	J	C
N	T	Z	K	A	V	I
P	L	Q	F	O	D	X
G	Y	B	U	H	S	

Puzzle No 47 Livingstone St, I Presume

Myers' shop is in Morton Street (clue 4) and Jordan owns shop 2 (clue 6). Shop 1 is in Livingstone Street (clue 3), so its proprietor isn't Bull (clue 3). No 5 is the off-licence and isn't owned by Bull (clues 3 and 4), so Gregson who runs the carpet shop (clue 1) doesn't own shop 1; thus shop 1 belongs to Lewis (clue 3) and is Spencer's and shop 5 is in Morton Street. Gregson's shop isn't numbered 3 or 6 (clue 1), so 4. Bull owns shop 3 (clue 4) and shop 6 belongs to Lewis. Shop 3 is the post office (clue 2). The chemist is in Henry Street (clue 5). Spencer doesn't own the antiques shop (clue 7), so the baker's. The chemist isn't shop 6 (clue 5), so 2 and (by elimination) shop 6 sells antiques. The shop in David Street isn't Bull's or Gregson's (clue 4), so Lewis'. The post office isn't in Victoria Street (clue 2), so Stanley Street and the carpet shop is in Victoria Street.

In summary:
1, Spencer, baker, Livingstone Street.
2, Jordan, chemist, Henry Street.
3, Bull, post office, Stanley Street.
4, Gregson, carpet shop, Victoria Street.
5, Myers, off-licence, Morton Street.
6, Lewis, antiques, David Street.

Puzzle No 48 Length is Strength

East's suit was hearts (clue 4) and Pass was North (clue 5). South whose long suit had only five cards (clue 3), wasn't Ruff (clue 1). Ruff's partner had the clubs and East's suit was hearts (clue 4), so Ruff wasn't West. Thus Ruff was East and West's suit was clubs (clue 1). South wasn't Trumpet (clue 2), so Bidding, whose partner Pass (clue 6) had an eight-card suit. By elimination, Trumpet was West. Pass's suit wasn't diamonds (clue 2), so spades and Bidding's was diamonds. Ruff had seven hearts (clue 1) and Trumpet six clubs.

In summary:
North, Pass, spades, 8.
East, Ruff, hearts, 7.
South, Bidding, diamonds, 5.
West, Trumpet, clubs, 6.

Puzzle No 49 Islands in the Sun

Keith's wife is Angela (clue 2) and Lance is Gail's father (clue 4). Violet's daughter is Fiona and her husband isn't Perry (clue 5), so Chris, whose son is Garry (clue 4). Darren's surname is Morris (clue 2) and Judy's is Langton (clue 3). Darren's mother isn't Angela (clue 2), so Bridget who (clue 6) went to Majorca. Violet isn't Mrs Chadwick whose holiday location was Crete (clue 5), so she's Mrs Durham and Mrs Chadwick is Angela. Judy's holiday wasn't in Cyprus (clue 3), so the Canaries and the Durhams went to Cyprus. Judy's husband isn't Lance (clue 4), so Perry and Lance is married to Bridget. Judy's son isn't Ian (clue 3), so Charles and her daughter is Rebecca (clue 1). By elimination, the Chadwick children are Ian and Janet.

In summary:
Chris & Violet Durham, Garry & Fiona, Cyprus.
Keith & Angela Chadwick, Ian & Janet, Crete.
Lance & Bridget Morris, Darren & Gail, Majorca.
Perry & Judy Langton, Charles & Rebecca, Canaries.

Puzzle No 50 Logical Moves

Marjorie's room was taken over by Jennifer whose original room was 237 (clue 3). Colin's original room was on an odd-numbered floor (clue 5). Room 421 which was reassigned to Howard (clue 4) was thus originally Stephen's. Stephen's complaint was snoring in the neighbouring room (clue 2). Colin's room was given to whoever complained about noise from the disco (clue 5), so to Marjorie. Howard didn't make the sea view complaint (clue 4) and wasn't the vertigo sufferer, who moved from 512 to 120 (clue 1), so he complained of the smell from the kitchens. Stephen wasn't given the room previously occupied by Howard (clue 6), so he took over room 237 and Colin took over Howard's room. Jennifer didn't complain about the disco noise (clue 5), so lack of a sea view. Colin's problem was thus vertigo. Marjorie's new room was 512 (clue 5), so Jennifer's was 334.

In summary:
Colin, vertigo, 120, Howard.
Howard, smell from kitchens, 421, Stephen.
Jennifer, no sea view, 334, Marjorie.
Marjorie, noise from disco, 512, Colin.
Stephen, snoring, 237, Jennifer.

Solutions

Puzzle No 51 Pop Classics

Player C didn't perform third (clue 1), first or second (clue 6). Player E didn't perform fifth (clue 1), so sixth (clue 6) and C was fifth. The piece played by the first soloist wasn't Yesterday or Yellow Submarine (clue 3), Penny Lane (clue 5) or Strawberry Fields (clue 6). The position of the soloist who played Eleanor Rigby wasn't F, B or C (clue 1), so A or E (clue 4). Player A wasn't first (clue 1), thus the first solo was A Hard Day's Night. The sixth piece wasn't Yellow Submarine or Yesterday (clue 3) or Strawberry Fields (clue 6), so Penny Lane, thus played by E; so Eleanor Rigby was played by A. Player at B was fourth (clue 4). Player A was second or third (clue 4), so the one who played Yesterday was third or fourth (clue 3). The one who played Yellow Submarine wasn't fifth (clue 3), so the fifth soloist played Strawberry Fields. The sixth instrument wasn't the oboe (clue 5) or clarinet (clue 6), so the flute. D played A Hard Day's Night (clue 2), so the second soloist played Yellow Submarine (clue 3). The Eleanor Rigby soloist was third (clue 4) and the Yesterday soloist fourth (clue 3). D played the violin (clue 5). The cellist wasn't fifth (clue 4) or third (clue 5), so fourth and the oboist was second (clue 5). The horn-player was fifth (clue 4). By elimination, Yellow Submarine was by player F and the clarinet solo was the third played.

In summary:
A, clarinet, Eleanor Rigby, third.
B, cello, Yesterday, fourth.
C, horn, Strawberry Fields, fifth.
D, violin, A Hard Day's Night, first.
E, flute, Penny Lane, sixth.
F, oboe, Yellow Submarine, second.

Puzzle No 52 Mountain Manoeuvres

Fiona Havelock is in the RLC (clue 3), so the female medic in the RAMC (clue 5) is Kate McMahon. The Gunner is in the RA (clue 4), so Corporal Andy Clive (clue 2) is in the RE. The Lieutenant was team leader (clue 1). Andy Clive wasn't the cook (clue 2), so the radio operator. By elimination, Kate McMahon is the Sergeant and Fiona Havelock the Lieutenant and Simon Wolfe is the Gunner and was the expedition cook.

In summary:
Corporal Andy Clive, RE, radio operator.
Gunner Simon Wolfe, RA, cook.
Lieutenant Fiona Havelock, RLC, team leader.
Sergeant Kate McMahon, RAMC, medic.

Puzzle No 53 Shopping for Lunch

The jeans were size 12 (clue 2). The garment from Last was size 10 and wasn't the minidress (clue 1) or swimsuit (clue 3), so the pinafore dress, which Diane bought (clue 5). Sarah's garment was size 14 (clue 4). The size 16 purchase wasn't Nikki's (clue 3), so Heather's from Atem (clue 1) and Nikki bought the jeans. Sarah didn't shop at D&B (clue 4), so Ebenham's and Nikki went to D&B. Heather bought the swimsuit (clue 1), so Sarah bought the minidress.

In summary:
Diane, Last, pinafore dress, size 10.
Heather, Atem, swimsuit, size 16.
Nikki, D&B, jeans, size 12.
Sarah, Ebenham's, minidress, size 14.

Puzzle No 54 Spice Girls Memories

Gail's surname is Nuttmeg (clue 3) and Laura's subject was English (clue 5). Miss Pepper whose subject was painting isn't Toni (clue 6), so Celia. The girl who was good at languages was either Gail or Toni, so (clue 1) Laura is Ms Turmerick and the model is Celia. Miss Cynamon the shop assistant (clue 2) is Toni. The former hockey player who is now a journalist (clue 4) is Gail. By elimination, Laura is a teacher and Toni's best subject was languages.

In summary:
Celia Pepper, painting, model.
Gail Nuttmeg, hockey, journalist.
Laura Turmerick, English, teacher.
Toni Cynamon, languages, shop assistant.

Puzzle No 55 Battle of Wits

The column referred to in clue 2, whose dates descend in chronological order, isn't column B, since 1066 is in square 6 (clue 1), column C, which contains two dates later than 1805 (clue 4), or column D, since the date in square 12 ends in an even digit (clue 5), so it's column A and square 9 thus contains 1805. Square 8 contains 1815 (clue 7). Thus the two dates separated by an exact number of hundreds of years, which are in squares 4 and 10 (clue 3) aren't 1415 and 1815, so 1642 and 1942. The latter isn't in square 4 (clue 4), so 10 and 1642 is in square 4. The left-hand neighbour of 1940 is 1759 (clue 6) and 1940 is in column C (clue 4), so it's in square 3 and 1759 is in square 2. Square 11 hasn't the 1916 (clue 5), so (clue 4) 1916 is in square 7. The only two remaining same-century dates are 1704 and 1746, so 1704 is in square 11 (clue 5) and 1746 in square 12. Square 1 has 1314 (clue 2) and 1415 is in square 5.

In summary:
1, 1314; 2, 1759; 3, 1940; 4, 1642.
5, 1415; 6, 1066; 7, 1916; 8, 1815.
9, 1805; 10, 1942; 11, 1704; 12, 1746.
Battles: 1066 Hastings; 1314 Bannockburn; 1415 Agincourt; 1642 Edgehill; 1704 Blenheim; 1746 Culloden; 1759 Quebec; 1805 Trafalgar; 1815 Waterloo; 1916 Somme; 1940 Battle of Britain; 1942 El Alamein.

Puzzle No 56 Home Town Politics

Nikolai represents Pulak (clue 2) and Pulaki represents Zivaz (clue 6). Boris Elski doesn't represent Crim (clue 3) or Elsk (intro), so Hatrov. The Liberal is Zivazi (clue 1) and the Democrat is Dmitri (clue 5). Boris isn't the Radical (clue 1) or the Nationalist (clue 4), so is the Progressive MBP. The Nationalist isn't Sergei (clue 4) or Nikolai (clue 5), so Vasili. Zivazi doesn't represent Pulak (clue 6), thus he isn't Nikolai (clue 2), so Sergei and Nikolai is the Radical. The MBP for

Elsk isn't Vasili (clue 2) or Dmitri (clue 5), so Sergei. By elimination, the MBP for Crim is Hatrovi and Nikolai is Crimi. Vasili isn't Hatrovi (clue 4), so Pulaki and Hatrovi is Dmitri.

In summary:
Boris Elski, Progressive, Hatrov.
Dmitri Hatrovi, Democratic, Crim.
Nikolai Crimi, Radical, Pulak.
Sergei Zivazi, Liberal, Elsk.
Vasili Pulaki, Nationalist, Zivaz.

Puzzle No 57 The Quick and Thurstead
Vince Well was doing 70mph (clue 3) and the driver in Plough Lane was doing 60mph (clue 6), so (clue 4) Andy Boate's speed in Storbury Road was 80mph and the Rover Metro driver was in Plough Lane. The Volvo 460 was speeding in Bridge Street (clue 1). The Ford Escort doing 50mph (clue 2) wasn't in Gallows Hill (clue 5), so Church Lane. Its driver wasn't Patsy O'Meta (clue 2) or Ken Limit (clue 5), so Doris Copp. Patsy O'Meta wasn't doing 40mph (clue 2), so 60mph and Ken Limit did 40mph. He wasn't in Gallows Hill (clue 5), so Bridge Street and Vince Well was in Gallows Hill. Vince Well's car wasn't the Ford Mondeo (clue 5), so the Honda Accord and Andy Boate drove the Ford Mondeo.

In summary:
Andy Boate, Ford Mondeo, 80mph, Storbury Road.
Doris Copp, Ford Escort, 50mph, Church Lane.
Ken Limit, Volvo 460, 40mph, Bridge Street.
Patsy O'Meta, Rover Metro, 60mph, Plough Lane.
Vince Well, Honda Accord, 70mph, Gallows Hill.

Puzzle No 58 Home on the Kibbutz
The Englishman arrived fourth (clue 4) and Levin is from Russia (clue 6). Aaron arrived fifth and isn't from Canada (clue 3), so Poland. Leon's surname is Cohen (clue 2) and Mr Goldstein was first to arrive (clue 5). Aaron's surname isn't Black (clue 3), so Blomberg. Mr Goldstein isn't David (clue 1), or Simon (clue 5), so Daniel. David's surname is thus Black (clue 1) and Simon's is Levin. The second to arrive wasn't David (clue 1) or Leon (clue 2), so Simon. David was third (clue 1) and Leon fourth. By elimination, David was from Canada.

In summary:
Aaron Blomberg, fifth, Poland.
Daniel Goldstein, first, USA.
David Black, third, Canada.
Leon Cohen, fourth, England.
Simon Levin, second, Russia.

Puzzle No 59 Props
The book is the prop for Scene 3 (clue 3) and the pot-plant is in the garden scene (clue 5). The prop for the hall scene isn't the cigarettes or the bottle and glasses (clue 4), so the gloves. The window-sill is used in Scene 2 (clue 2) and the coffee-table is used in the study scene (clue 6). The gloves won't be on the cupboard or mantelpiece (clue 4), so on the chair in the hall. The prop for the study scene isn't the

book (clue 3) or cigarettes (clues 4 and 6), so the bottle and glasses. By elimination, the pot-plant is on the window-sill and the cupboard is used in Scene 3. The prop in Scene 1 isn't the bottle and glasses (clue 1), so cigarettes and the bottle and glasses are in Scene 5. Scene 1 isn't in the bedroom (clue 1), so the drawing-room and Scene 3 is in the bedroom.

In summary:
Scene 1, drawing-room, cigarettes on the mantelpiece.
Scene 2, garden, pot-plant on the window-sill.
Scene 3, bedroom, book on the cupboard.
Scene 4, hall, gloves on the chair.
Scene 5, study, bottle and glasses on the coffee-table.

Puzzle No 60 Holy Order
The surname of the first baby to be baptised was Cross and this isn't James (clue 3), so (clue 5) Anne was baptised on March 15th and James was also baptised in March; not on the 1st (clue 1), so the 29th. The infants baptised on March 1st and May 10th (clue 1) are two of Edward, Eleanor and Emma. James isn't Christian (clue 5), so (clue 4) Emma wasn't baptised on either March 1st or May 10th. Eleanor wasn't baptised in May (clue 7), so on March 1st and Edward on May 10th. The Cross daughter baptised on February 1st wasn't Emma (clue 4), so Geraldine. Baby Parsons was baptised on February 15th (clue 2). Emma's Christening wasn't on February 15th or April 26th (clue 4), so April 12th and the boy named Christian is Edward. Mark wasn't Christened on February 15th (clue 6), so April 26th. Thus Emma is Font (clue 6) and James's surname is Godfather. Anthony is baby Parsons and Anne's surname is Jordan (clue 7). Eleanor's surname isn't Dove (clue 7), so Waters and Mark's is Dove.

In summary:
February 1st, Geraldine Cross.
February 15th, Anthony Parsons.
March 1st, Eleanor Waters.
March 15th, Anne Jordan.
March 29th, James Godfather.
April 12th, Emma Font.
April 26th, Mark Dove.
May 10th, Edward Christian.

Puzzle No 61 The Y Files
The crater in the mountainside was discovered near Bizarre (clue 5) and Enigma is in Oregon (clue 6). The glowing forest was located in Montana, but not near Weirdsville or Strangeleigh (clue 1), so Arkane. Strangeleigh was visited by Mildew and Scilly at 2.07pm (clue 2), thus the investigation at 10.31am wasn't in Strangeleigh or Weirdsville (clue 3). So Bizarre is in Ohio and is the location of the case that began at 10.31am. The lights in the sky investigation began at 6.48am (clue 5). Arkane wasn't visited at 2.07pm, 10.31am or 11.32am (clue 1), so 4.16pm. The 11.32am investigation wasn't in Weirdsville (clue 1), so Enigma and the Weirdsville investigation started at 6.48am. The 2.07pm case didn't involve disappearing families (clue 2), so the wreckage in the

Solutions

desert and the disappearing families case was at 11.32am. The wreckage in the desert wasn't in Kansas (clue 4), so New Mexico and the lights in the sky investigation was in Kansas.

In summary:
Arkane, Montana, 4.16pm, glowing forest.
Bizarre, Ohio, 10.31am, crater in mountainside.
Enigma, Oregon, 11.32am, disappearing families.
Strangeleigh, New Mexico, 2.07pm, wreckage in desert.
Weirdsville, Kansas, 6.48am, lights in sky.

Puzzle No 62 Prodigal Prodigies
Anna works in Paris (clue 6), so the girl in Moscow (clue 3) is Joan the flute player (clue 2). The resident of New York isn't Moira (clue 7), so Nancy (clue 3), the theatrical agent (clue 1). The girl who played clarinet works in London (clue 4). The pianist became a courier (clue 5), so Moira is the geologist based in Rome (clue 8) and the former pianist is Anna. The former clarinettist isn't the diplomat (clue 4), so a journalist and the diplomat is Joan. The journalist is Kathleen. Nancy wasn't the violinist (clue 3), so a singer and the violinist was Moira.

In summary:
Anna, piano, Paris, courier.
Joan, flute, Moscow, diplomat.
Kathleen, clarinet, London, journalist.
Moira, violin, Rome, geologist.
Nancy, singing, New York, theatrical agent.

Puzzle No 63 Expert Opinion
Lavinia knows all about porcelain (clue 2) and silver was assessed by the second expert (clue 6). Jonathan was the first featured (clue 4). His area of expertise isn't dolls (clue 1), nor is he Pride, the firearms expert (clue 5), so Jonathan is the furniture expert. Ernest Dell isn't an expert on dolls (clue 1), so silver and the expert on dolls was seen third and is Highfield (clue 3). Pride is male (clue 5), so he's Angus. By elimination, the doll expert is Tessa. Angus wasn't featured fourth (clue 5), so fifth and Lavinia was fourth. Lavinia's surname is Carrow (clue 5), so Jonathan's is Goodison.

In summary:
Angus Pride, firearms, fifth.
Ernest Dell, silver, second.
Jonathan Goodison, furniture, first.
Lavinia Carrow, porcelain, fourth.
Tessa Highfield, dolls, third.

Puzzle No 64 Mothers' Day
Jan's daughter's name begins with an L (clue 2) and Sandra is Gemma's mother (clue 6). Katy's mother isn't Carol (clue 4) or Brenda (clue 5), so Pat and Katy's brother is thus George (clue 3). Thomas' treat was breakfast in bed (clue 1) and Lucy's was a cup of tea (clue 3). Katy and George didn't cook lunch (clue 4) or wash up (clue 5), so put flowers in the bedroom. Laura's brother is Mark (clue 1). Sarah's isn't Thomas or James (clue 1), so Ben. By elimination, Thomas is Gemma's brother and

Lucy's brother is James. Their mum isn't Jan (clue 2), so Jan's daughter is Laura. Carol's son isn't James (clue 4), so Ben who (by elimination) did the washing up. By elimination, James's mother is Brenda and Jan's children cooked lunch.

In summary:
Brenda, James and Lucy, cup of tea in bed.
Carol, Ben and Sarah, washing up.
Jan, Mark and Laura, cooking lunch.
Pat, George and Katy, flowers in bedroom.
Sandra, Thomas and Gemma, breakfast in bed.

Puzzle No 65 Sick Soldiers
Private Troop with a cut finger isn't in position 6 (clue 4) or position 4 (clue 2). The man in position 6 hasn't a sore throat (clue 1), earache (clue 2), a boil (clue 3) or stomach ache (clue 4), so a bruised toe. The man with the boil is in position 5 (clue 3) and Private Martial in position 4. Fortress isn't in position 4 and the man with earache isn't Martial (clue 2), so the man with earache is in either position 1 or 2 and Fortress is in 2 or 3. Troop isn't in 3 (clue 4), so 1 or 2. If Troop is in position 2, Fortress is in 3 and the man with earache in 1. But the man with earache is ahead of Fortress (clue 2), thus Troop is in position 1, Fortress in 3 and the man with earache in 2. The man with a stomach ache is Fortress (clue 4). The man with a sore throat is Martial (clue 1) and Rampart has a bruised toe, so Battle has earache and Busby has a boil.

In summary:
1, Troop, cut finger.
2, Battle, earache.
3, Fortress, stomach ache.
4, Martial, sore throat.
5, Busby, boil.
6, Rampart, bruised toe.

Puzzle No 66 In Triplicate
Gavin's senior sibling is Beryl (clue 3), Joyce's surname is Perry (clue 4) and Henry has an older brother (clue 5). Alice Rudge's middle sibling isn't Frank (clue 6), so Irene. Their junior sibling is male (clue 5) and isn't Keith (clue 6), so Oscar. The senior Quinn is female (clue 1). Marie's surname is Smith (clue 2). Joyce's senior isn't Colin, whose junior sibling is Nancy (clue 4), so Colin's surname is Tyler. Beryl's surname isn't Smith (clues 2 and 3), so Quinn. Her junior sibling isn't Lydia (clue 1), so Keith and Lydia's surname is Perry. Dinah isn't the senior Smith (clue 2), so her surname is Perry and Marie's senior sibling is Edwin. Henry's surname isn't Tyler (clue 5), so Smith and Frank's is Tyler.

In summary:
Alice, Irene and Oscar Rudge.
Beryl, Gavin and Keith Quinn.
Colin, Frank and Nancy Tyler.
Dinah, Joyce and Lydia Perry.
Edwin, Henry and Marie Smith.

Solutions

Puzzle No 67 Flying a Kite

Henry, whose kite is orange, isn't 8 or 11 (clue 1). The blue kite belongs to the child aged 9 (clue 3), so Henry is 10. Kite B is red and doesn't belong to the 8-year-old (clue 2), so its owner is 11 and Katie is 9. Jack isn't 11 (clue 4), so 8 and Marie is 11. Jack's kite isn't A (clue 4), so C (clue 1) and (by elimination) is yellow. Katie's kite isn't D (clue 3), so A and D is Henry's.

In summary:
A, Katie, 9, blue.
B, Marie, 11, red.
C, Jack, 8, yellow.
D, Henry, 10, orange.

Puzzle No 68 Egon Toste

Toby Cameron is famous for his beef Wellington (clue 1) and Toni Giordano is the chef at Giordano's (clue 2). Game pie is recommended at The Vineyard whose chef is neither Pierre Laval nor Philippe Legrand (clue 5), so Antoine Marron, whose restaurant got two stars (clue 3). The Arcadia got one star (clue 4) and Gorsehill Manor four or five (clue 1). The three-star restaurant isn't Giordano's (clue 2), so La Pergola. The lemon surprise isn't at Gorsehill Manor (clue 1), Giordano's (clue 2) or La Pergola (clue 6), so the Arcadia. Toby Cameron doesn't work at Gorsehill Manor (clue 1), so La Pergola. The Arcadia's chef isn't Philippe Legrand (clue 4), so Pierre Laval and Gorsehill Manor's is Philippe Legrand. His speciality isn't ragout of lamb (clue 4), so pears in port, thus his restaurant got four stars (clue 6) and Giordano's has five.

In summary:
Arcadia, Pierre Laval, one star, lemon surprise.
Giordano's, Toni Giordano, five stars, ragout of lamb.
Gorsehill Manor, Philippe Legrand, four stars, pears in port.
La Pergola, Toby Cameron, three stars, beef Wellington.
The Vineyard, Antoine Marron, two stars, game pie.

Puzzle No 69 Starbattles

The weapon in Starbattle I is the Disintegrator Gun (clue 1). In Starbattle III it isn't the alien mercenaries (clue 3), nor since the villain in that film is male (clue 3), Lady Cathadon's mutant warriors (clue 2). General Zorkh dies in a powersword fight (clue 1). The leader of the killer robots leaps from a cliff (clue 6), so the villain in Starbattle III who dies in a starfighter dogfight (clue 3) uses the Mind Control Ray. He isn't Duke Darvad (clue 7), so Prince Gordan. Starbattle V has a male villain (clue 5). Lady Cathadon doesn't appear in Starbattle II (clue 2), so Starbattle IV. Her starcruiser doesn't explode (clue 4), so her planet explodes. The villain in Starbattle I doesn't die in a powersword fight (clue 1) or by jumping from the cliff (clue 6), so in an exploding starcruiser. Princess Kalka doesn't jump from the cliff (clue 6), so dies in the starcruiser explosion and Duke Darvad leaps from a cliff. The weapon in Starbattle V isn't the alien mercenaries (clue 5), so is the killer robots and the alien mercenaries are in Starbattle II.

In summary:

Starbattle I, Princess Kalka, Disintegrator Gun, starcruiser explodes.
Starbattle II, General Zorkh, alien mercenaries, powersword fight.
Starbattle III, Prince Gordan, Mind Control Ray, starfighter dogfight.
Starbattle IV, Lady Cathadon, mutant warriors, planet explodes.
Starbattle V, Duke Darvad, killer robots, jumps off cliff.

Puzzle No 70 Flatmates

John and his wife are in flat 6 (clue 4) and Madge and her husband in flat 5 (clue 5), so (clue 1) Albert and Violet are in flat 4 and the Simpsons in flat 1. Donald Williams doesn't live in flat 5 (clue 5), so both the Williamses and the Robinses live on the ground floor. Margaret Dixon is thus in flat 6 (clue 2). The couple named Lewis aren't in flat 4 (clue 3), so flat 5. By elimination, Albert is Mr Gordon, so (clue 6) Leonard is in flat 3. By elimination, he's Mr Robins and Donald lives in flat 2. Bernard has a first floor flat (clue 7), thus he's in flat 5, Henry is Mr Simpson and Joan is Mrs Williams. Henry's wife isn't Ella and Sarah is Mrs Robins (clue 8), so Ella and Sarah is Mrs Robins.

In summary:
Flat 1, Henry and Ella Simpson.
Flat 2, Donald and Joan Williams.
Flat 3, Leonard and Sarah Robins.
Flat 4, Albert and Violet Gordon.
Flat 5, Bernard and Madge Lewis.
Flat 6, John and Margaret Dixon.

Puzzle No 71 By the Seaside

The mother of child D isn't in deck-chairs 4 (clue 1), 1 or 2 (clue 2), so 3. Thus Jill is in 2 (clue 2) and Emma's mum in 1. Jack is the son of Francesca (clue 3) who isn't in 3 (clue 3), so 4. Child D isn't Karen (clue 4), so Damien and Karen's mother is Jill. Karen isn't B (clue 1), so A (clue 4) and Lesley is the mother of C who is thus Emma. By elimination, Damien's mother is Sally and Jack is child B.

In summary:
A, Karen, 2, Jill.
B, Jack, 4, Francesca.
C, Emma, 1, Lesley.
D, Damien, 3, Sally.

Puzzle No 72 Love Pays the Bills

'Daydream' was bought by Lovebirds (clue 3), Soulmates paid £140 (clue 5) and Loving Couples bought a story in May for less than £150 (clue 6). 'Street Scene' sold for £160 but not to Cupid (clue 4), so Eternal Love. 'Street Scene' wasn't sold in May (clues 4 and 6). 'The Orchid' was sold in April (clue 1), not to Cupid (clue 4), so Soulmates. The February story sold for £100 (clue 2). 'Street Scene' didn't sell in January (clue 4), so March and Cupid bought the February story. By elimination, 'Daydream' was sold in January. The story sold in May wasn't

Solutions

'Point Of View' (clue 1), so 'Partners' and 'Point Of View' was sold in February. 'Partners' sold for £120 (clue 6) and 'Daydream' for £180.

In summary:
January, 'Daydream', Lovebirds, £180.
February, 'Point Of View', Cupid, £100.
March, 'Street Scene', Eternal Love, £160.
April, 'The Orchid', Soulmates, £140.
May, 'Partners', Loving Couples, £120.

Puzzle No 73 Game On

The game which uses the bunch of feathers isn't brole casting (clue 1), fryle turling (clue 2), throle clogging or doodle knocking (clue 6), so stile haggling. The village where this is played isn't Backwater or Strangeham (clue 1), Laffiton (clue 4) or Playwick (clue 5), so Oddleigh. Since brole casting in Laffiton (clue 4) doesn't make use of the bow and arrow (clue 1), it doesn't make use of the turnip (clue 5). Nor does it use the pig's bladder or the ham bone (clue 4), so the horseshoe. The bow and arrow and turnip don't feature in Backwater (clue 1) or Playwick (clue 5), so Strangeham. The pig's bladder isn't used in Playwick (clue 1), so Backwater and Playwick's game involves the ham bone. Backwater's doesn't use the bucket (clue 1), wooden stool (clue 3) or milk churn (clue 4), so a shepherd's crook. The milk churn isn't used at Oddleigh or Playwick (clue 4), so it's linked with the horseshoe. The bucket isn't used in doodle knocking (clue 6), so fryle turling, which isn't Backwater's game (clue 1). The bow and arrow aren't used in throle clogging (clue 1), so doodle knocking which is thus Strangeham's game. By elimination, Backwater's game is throle clogging, fryle turling is played at Playwick and the wooden stool is used in stile haggling.

In summary:
Backwater, throle clogging, pig's bladder, shepherd's crook.
Laffiton, brole casting, horseshoe, milk churn.
Oddleigh, stile haggling, bunch of feathers, wooden stool.
Playwick, fryle turling, ham bone, bucket.
Strangeham, doodle knocking, turnip, bow and arrow.

Puzzle No 74 Les Chattaway

The 3.05 (first) guest will talk for 8 minutes (clue 1), Kathleen Miller for 14 (clue 2) and the toy collector for 11 minutes (clue 6). Dr John Hobbs will talk on health (clue 1). The man talking about his book of poems at 3.40 isn't on for 12 minutes (clue 3), so 10 and isn't Arthur Shelton (clue 5), so Gordon Palmer. The doctor won't talk for 8 minutes (clue 1), so 12. Mrs Miller isn't on at 3.20 (clue 2) or 4.35 (clue 4), so 4.05. She isn't talking about local history (clue 4), so her work overseas and the local history enthusiast is on at 3.05. The person allocated 11 minutes isn't Jane Neville (clue 6), so Arthur Shelton and Miss Neville is the 3.05 guest. The 4.35 guest hasn't been allocated 12 minutes (clue 4), so 11 minutes and Dr Hobbs will speak for 12 minutes.

In summary:
3.05, Jane Neville, local history, 8 minutes.
3.20, Dr John Hobbs, health, 12 minutes.
3.40, Gordon Palmer, book of poems, 10 minutes.
4.05, Kathleen Miller, work overseas, 14 minutes.
4.35, Arthur Shelton, toy collection, 11 minutes.

Puzzle No 75 Blewbludd Court

The shoemaker's shop is at number 2 (clue 3) and Catesby & Doone is at number 5 (clue 4). Rudiger & Scales isn't a shoemaker's or barber's and doesn't sell books or wine and isn't at number 1 (clue 7). From clues 3 and 7, Rudiger & Scales isn't at number 4, so at either number 3 or number 6. The pharmacy is opposite Prior & Quarles which isn't at number 1 or 4 (clue 6), so (by elimination) Rudiger & Scales is the gunsmith's. Thus (clue 2) Rudiger & Scales is at number 3 and (clue 7) the bookshop at number 1. The barber's is thus at number 4 (clue 1) and the wine merchant at number 6. Prior & Quarles isn't the pharmacy, bookseller or barber's shop (clue 6); nor (length of name) is it the shoemaker's shop (clue 3), so it's the wine merchant and (clue 6) Catesby & Doone is the pharmacy. Halkett & Jocelyn isn't the shoemaker's shop (clue 3) or the bookseller (clue 5), so the barber's shop, thus Foxley & Glossin is the bookseller and Launce & Manders the shoemaker's shop.

In summary:
1, Foxley & Glossin, bookseller.
2, Launce & Manders, shoemaker.
3, Rudiger & Scales, gunsmith.
4, Halkett & Jocelyn, barber.
5, Catesby & Doone, pharmacy.
6, Prior & Quarles, wine merchant.

Puzzle No 76 Telecops I

Nick is the security chief (clue 5) and Annie is Gahagan (clue 8). McClintock the FBI agent isn't Pete (clue 7) or Ben (clue 6), so Scott and is based in Anchorage (clue 2). The Chicago detective is Zitkin (clue 3). There is no series with an 8-letter title, so Blackwood isn't set in Las Vegas (clue 6), nor is it set in Memphis (clue 1), so it's based in Brewerton and thus concerns the Chief of Police (clue 4). Annie Gahagan isn't a private eye (clue 8), so a Detective Lieutenant. The Las Vegas-based detective isn't Torricelli (clue 6), so Gahagan and Ben is Zitkin. By elimination, Nick is based in Memphis and is Torricelli, Blackwood is Pete and Zitkin is the private eye.

In summary:
Blackwood, Pete, Chief of Police, Brewerton.
Gahagan, Annie, Detective Lieutenant, Las Vegas.
McClintock, Scott, FBI agent, Anchorage.
Torricelli, Nick, security chief, Memphis.
Zitkin, Ben, private eye, Chicago.

Solutions

Puzzle No 77 Telecops II

Ben Zitkin is divorced (clue 5) and Nick Torricelli is a bad cook (clue 7). The separated telecop who does correspondence courses isn't Scott who runs a youth club or Pete Blackwood (clue 3 and previous problem), so Annie Gahagan who (clue 4) doesn't read whodunnits. The single parent plays chess (clue 1) and computers is the hobby of the person giving up smoking (clue 2), so Annie's hobby is judo. Scott isn't superstitious (clue 6), so acrophobic and Pete is superstitious. By elimination, Ben is giving up smoking. Pete's hobby isn't chess (clue 1), so he reads whodunnits and Nick plays chess. Pete doesn't have an invalid spouse (clue 6), so he's married with a family and Scott has an invalid spouse.

In summary:
Annie, separated, judo, correspondence courses.
Ben, divorced, computers, giving up smoking.
Nick, single parent, chess, bad cook.
Pete, married with family, whodunnits, superstitious.
Scott, invalid spouse, youth club, acrophobic.

Puzzle No 78 Every One a Winner

The vegetables grown on allotment 1 rented by Sprouting (clue 5), aren't Tom's beetroots (clue 1), peas (clue 2), leeks (clue 3), cauliflowers (clue 4) or potatoes (clue 6), so turnips. Peas are grown on allotment 2 (clue 2). Allotment 3 doesn't grow beetroots (clue 1), cauliflowers (clue 4) or potatoes (clue 6), so leeks. Patch grows peas (clue 3) and John is Sprouting. Eddie Greenfinger thus has allotment 3 (clue 4) and cauliflowers grow on allotment 6. Wilf is Patch (clue 6). Tilth has allotment 5 (clue 4) which doesn't grow beetroots (clue 1), so the potatoes. By elimination, Tom has allotment 4. Percy's allotment isn't 5 (clue 1), so 6 and Charlie's is 5. Percy isn't Plant (clue 1), so Gardiner and Tom is Plant.

In summary:
1, John Sprouting, turnips.
2, Wilf Patch, peas.
3, Eddie Greenfinger, leeks.
4, Tom Plant, beetroots.
5, Charlie Tilth, potatoes.
6, Percy Gardiner, cauliflowers.

Puzzle No 79 Words of Wisdom

The boy in seat D isn't Sean (clue 2), Darren (clue 3) or Ron (clue 5), so Jack. The 11-year-old didn't speak fourth (clue 3), so the 10-year-old didn't speak third (clue 4). Nor did the 10-year-old speak first (clue 3) or fourth (clue 4), so second and Darren was first (clue 3). By elimination, Darren is 13. He wasn't in seat A (clue 1), so B (clue 3) and Jack is 10. Sean was in seat C (clue 2) and Ron in A (clue 5). Sean didn't speak third (clue 1), so fourth and Ron was third. Jack explained the internet (clue 2). Sean didn't explain CD-ROM (clue 6), so (clue 5) sound bite and Darren described cyberspace; thus Ron explained CD-ROM.

In summary:
A, Ron, 11, CD-ROM, third.
B, Darren, 13, cyberspace, first.
C, Sean, 12, sound bite, fourth.
D, Jack, 10, internet, second.

Puzzle No 80 The Wisdom of Sophocles

The third new face was the club secretary (clue 2), the fifth was Kenny Liftham (clue 5) and the second Mal Function (clue 6). Al Spottam the new youth organiser wasn't appointed first, third or fourth (clue 1), so second and Dick Lining the team manager was first (clue 1). The new chief coach wasn't appointed fifth (clue 3), so fourth and Kenny Liftham is the new physiotherapist who replaced Perry Luss. The sacked club secretary wasn't Luke Down (clue 2), so A Paul Ling, whose replacement was Bobby Knupp (clue 4). Thus the former chief coach was Luke Down, who wasn't replaced by Phil Lipp (clue 2), so Benny Fitt. Phil Lipp is the new team manager.

In summary:
A Paul Ling, club secretary, Bobby Knupp, third.
Dick Lining, team manager, Phil Lipp, first.
Luke Down, chief coach, Benny Fitt, fourth.
Mal Function, youth organiser, Al Spottam, second.
Perry Luss, physiotherapist, Kenny Liftham, fifth.

Puzzle No 81 Bob's Jobs

Bob works at Highfield on Mondays (clue 4) and his Friday employer is Mr Little (clue 5), so (clue 1) he works at West Winds on Tuesday and tends the garden of Mr Gross the stockbroker on Thursday. Ten Gables belongs to the garage owner (clue 2). Mr Gross isn't at Greenlea (clue 6), so Pinewood and (clue 3) the caravan manufacturer is Mr Little. By elimination, Wednesdays are spent at Ten Gables and Mr Little lives at Greenlea. The novelist isn't the Monday employer (clue 7), so owns West Winds. Highfield is thus the home of the airline pilot, who (clue 7) is Mr Longman. Bob's Tuesday employer isn't Mr Short (clue 4), so Mr Burley and Mr Short is the garage owner.

In summary:
Monday, Highfield, Mr Longman, airline pilot.
Tuesday, West Winds, Mr Burley, novelist.
Wednesday, Ten Gables, Mr Short, garage owner.
Thursday, Pinewood, Mr Gross, stockbroker.
Friday, Greenlea, Mr Little, caravan manufacturer.

Puzzle No 82 The Paragon in Character

Alljack had a Liverpool accent (clue 5) and Egbert was Jellyby (clue 6). Zebedee with the Manchester accent wasn't Skimpole the bookmaker (clue 3) or Uploft (clue 5), so Pinchbeck. The taxi-driver's first name was Jesse (clue 4) and the gardener spoke with a Newcastle accent (clue 6). Zebedee wasn't the sailor (clue 2), so the clergyman. The Geordie gardener wasn't

Solutions

Jellyby (clue 6), so Uploft. By elimination, Jellyby was the sailor and Jesse was Alljack. Barnaby was Uploft (clue 1) and Tobias was Skimpole (clue 1), so Birmingham. Skimpole's accent wasn't from Bristol (clue 1), so Birmingham. By elimination, Egbert had the Bristol accent.

In summary:
Barnaby Uploft, gardener, Newcastle.
Egbert Jellyby, sailor, Bristol.
Jesse Alljack, taxi-driver, Liverpool.
Tobias Skimpole, bookmaker, Birmingham.
Zebedee Pinchbeck, clergyman, Manchester.

Puzzle No 83 Game, Set and Match

Tom won the final with a service ace (clue 1) and Thorpe was beaten by a passing shot (clue 6). Dennison was his third-round opponent and didn't bring about his own downfall (clue 2), so was beaten by the drop shot. Paul was Tom's semi-final opponent (clue 3). The volley wasn't netted in the first or second rounds (clue 4), so the semi-final. Gavin Rankin played in the final (clue 4), Paul netted the volley and Tarquin was the third-round opponent. The second-round opponent wasn't Wayne (clue 5), so Michael and Wayne was the first-round loser. Thorpe isn't Michael (clue 6), so Wayne and Michael lost by double-faulting. Paul isn't Hurst (clue 5), so Wilby and Michael is Hurst.

In summary:
First round, Wayne Thorpe, passing shot.
Second round, Michael Hurst, opponent double-faulted.
Third round, Tarquin Dennison, drop-shot.
Semi-final, Paul Wilby, opponent netted volley.
Final, Gavin Rankin, ace serve.

Puzzle No 84 The First Millennium

Wat proposed the South Field structure (clue 2) and Egbert's was to cost an odd number of silver pieces (clue 3). The 220-piece project near the church wasn't proposed by Hubert or Oswin (clue 1), so was Wilfred's duck-pond (clue 6). The stone bridge was to be at the river (clue 4). The cow-byre wasn't to be at Manor Farm (clue 1) or the Abbey (clue 4), so South Field. The 20-piece option (cheapest) wasn't proposed by Oswin or Hubert (clue 1) or Egbert (clue 3), so Wat. Egbert's odd-number price was higher than that for the granary (clue 3), so 335 pieces. It wasn't the pig-sty (clue 5), so the stone bridge across the river. The 65-piece project wasn't the granary (clue 5), so the pig-sty and the granary cost was 170 silver pieces. Oswin thus proposed the granary (clue 1) and Hubert the pig-sty. The granary wasn't to be at Manor Farm (clue 1), so the Abbey and the pig-sty was to be at Manor Farm.

In summary:
Egbert, stone bridge, river, 335 silver pieces.
Hubert, pig-sty, Manor Farm, 65 silver pieces.
Oswin, granary, Abbey, 170 silver pieces.
Wat, cow-byre, South Field, 20 silver pieces.
Wilfred, duck-pond, church, 220 silver pieces.

Puzzle No 85 Turn of the Centurion

Century III's banner was blue (clue 3). Century I's wasn't green (clue 1), yellow (clue 3) or red (clue 4), so white. Billius was the centurion of century II (clue 2). The banner of century II wasn't green (clue 1) or red (clue 4), so yellow and the device on century I's banner was the hawk (clue 3). The device on century V's wasn't the lion (clue 1), serpent (clue 4) or leopard (clue 5), so bear. Century IV's device wasn't the lion (clue 1) or serpent (clue 5), so leopard. Brutus didn't command the century with the serpent device (clue 1), so the lion was the device of century III and century II's was the serpent. Thus Brutus was the centurion of century IV and V's banner was green (clue 1). Century I's centurion wasn't Stentorius (clue 4) or Decibillius (clue 5), so Raucus. Decibillius didn't command century V (clue 5), so century III and Stentorius commanded century V. The red banner belonged to century IV.

In summary:
I, Raucus, white, hawk.
II, Billius, yellow, serpent.
III, Decibillius, blue, lion.
IV, Brutus, red, leopard.
V, Stentorius, green, bear.

Puzzle No 86 Kicking the Habit

Lesley smokes 40 a day (clue 4). The woman who smokes 35 a day isn't Maggie (clue 3), so Joy. The 20-a-day smoker's longest period without is 6 days (clue 5). This person didn't try to stop 7 or 8 times (clue 5) or 4 (clue 6). Since the smoker who tried to stop 5 times once lasted 14 days (clue 1), the 20-a-day smoker stopped 6 times and (clue 5) whoever lasted out 12 days stopped 8 times. The person who has quit 4 times hasn't gone a maximum of 8 days (clue 6), so 10 days and (by elimination) whoever stopped 7 times once went 8 days without. The 30-a-day smoker has quit 4 times (clue 2), so (clue 6) Charles smokes 20 a day. The 30-a-day smoker isn't Ben (clue 2), so Maggie and Ben's daily total is 25. Lesley has given up 7 times and Joy 8 times (clue 4), so Ben has given up 5 times.

In summary:
Ben, 25 a day, 5 times, 14 days.
Charles, 20 a day, 6 times, 6 days.
Joy, 35 a day, 8 times, 12 days.
Lesley, 40 a day, 7 times, 8 days.
Maggie, 30 a day, 4 times, 10 days.

Puzzle No 87 Snakes and Ladders

The player on square 84 moved to 53 (clue 6). Brian who started on square 65 threw an even number (clue 1), so didn't go to square 35 (clue 4). He didn't end on square 49 (clue 1) or 21 (clue 3), so square 89. Thus he didn't throw a 6 (clue 1), so a 4. The throw of 5 took one player to square 35 (clue 4), so the person who ended on 21 and threw an odd number but not 3 (clue 3), threw a 1. He or she didn't start on 12 (clue 5) or 73 (clue 2), so 6. The player who threw a 1 is either Martin or Wendy (clue 3), so Ellen who threw a lower number than Brian (clue 1), threw a 3. Dave thus started on 73 (clue 2) and Martin threw a 1. The person who threw a 5 wasn't Wendy (clue 4), so Dave. The player who started on 12 wasn't Wendy (clue 5), so Ellen. By elimination, Ellen ended her turn via a ladder on 49 and the player who took a snake to 53 was Wendy, who threw a 6.

In summary:
Brian, threw 4, ladder from 65 to 89.
Dave, threw 5, snake from 73 to 35.
Ellen, threw 3, ladder from 12 to 49.
Martin, threw 1, ladder from 6 to 21.
Wendy, threw 6, snake from 84 to 53.

Puzzle No 88 Safe...

Neither Wise nor Loyell has to dial a 3 (clue 3), so the other three men do and the 3 appears as a first digit, a second digit and a third (clue 1). The man with 3 as his third digit isn't Parfitt (clue 4), or Sphinx (clue 6), so Trustey, whose first digit is 0 (clue 2). Since Wise's three read in ascending order (clue 6), his second isn't 0 or 4; nor is it 3 (clue 3). Sphinx's third digit is two lower than Wise's (clue 6), so Wise's second is 2 and Sphinx's third is 0. Since Wise has no 3 in his combination, his third digit is 4 and his first is 1 (clue 6). The 3 in second position doesn't follow a 2 (clue 5) or another 3 (clue 1). Trustey's third is a 3 (clue 1), so the 3 in second position must follow an initial 4. This isn't part of Loyell's combination (clue 3), nor is Loyell's first digit a 3; thus Loyell's first is a 2 and (clue 1) his third is 1. Parfitt's third is thus 2 (clue 4) and his first digit is 4, so his second is 3. By elimination, Sphinx's first is 3, so Trustey's second is 4 (clue 7). Sphinx's second isn't 0 (clue 1), so 1 and Loyell's second is 0.

In summary:
Loyell, 2, 0, 1.
Parfitt, 4, 3, 2.
Sphinx, 3, 1, 0.
Trustey, 0, 4, 3.
Wise, 1, 2, 4.

Puzzle No 89 ...keeping

Wise has 6 as his fourth digit (clue 2). The 7 in fourth position belongs to Parfitt or Trustey and Parfitt's combination doesn't include a 7 (clue 3) so Loyell, whose fourth digit is the same as Parfitt's fifth (clue 4), hasn't a 7 as his fourth. Thus Sphinx's fourth is 7 (clue 1). Wise's fifth is 8 (clue 6), so the man whose fifth is 7 is Loyell. The man with 7 as his sixth digit isn't Parfitt or Trustey (clue 3), so Wise. Parfitt's fifth isn't 5 (clue 5) and Wise's fourth is a 6, thus Parfitt's fifth isn't 6 (clue 4), so 9 and 9 is Loyell's fourth. Trustey's fourth isn't 5 (clue 7), so 8 and Parfitt's is 5 (clue 1). Sphinx's fifth is 6 (clue 7), so Trustey's is 5. Loyell's sixth isn't 5 (clue 8), so the remaining 5 is in Sphinx's combination. Thus (clue 2) Parfitt's sixth digit is 6. Loyell already has a 9, so by elimination, his sixth digit is 8 and Trustey's sixth is 9.

In summary:
Loyell, 9, 7, 8.
Parfitt, 5, 9, 6.
Sphinx, 7, 6, 5.
Trustey, 8, 5, 9.
Wise, 6, 8, 7.

Puzzle No 90 Claycaster Museums

A C Quire is curator of the Clayshire Regiment Museum (clue 1) and the Social History Museum is in Geffrye Lane (clue 4), so G Ather's museum in Wallace Street which doesn't have the town name in its title (clue 3) is the Natural History Museum. O B Tain is curator of the ex-warehouse (clue 3). The curator of the Claycaster Art Museum in the old fire station (clue 4) isn't H Oard (clue 4), so S E Cure. The museum in Iveagh Square was formerly a mansion (clue 1), so the Claycaster Art Museum is in Horniman Street (clue 2). The museum in Wallace Street wasn't a courthouse (clue 3), so a church. The Clayshire Regiment Museum isn't in the former mansion (clue 1), so it was a courthouse and (by elimination) is in St Bride's Green. By elimination, the Claycaster Museum is in Iveagh Square with H Oard as curator and the Social History Museum's curator is O B Tain.

In summary:
Claycaster Museum, mansion, Iveagh Square, H Oard.
Claycaster Art Museum, fire station, Horniman St, S E Cure.
Clayshire Regiment Museum, courthouse, St Bride's Green, A C Quire.
Natural History Museum, church, Wallace St, G Ather.
Social History Museum, warehouse, Geffrye Lane, O B Tain.

Puzzle No 91 Hope Springs Eternal

Simon's side just avoided relegation (clue 4) and Flagg's finished in mid-table (clue 5). Carl Stand's weren't promoted or relegated (clue 6), so just missed promotion. Midchester City were relegated (clue 1). Willie is the Grayburn Athletic fan (clue 5) and Turnstyle supports Swanfield United (clue 2). Padbury Rovers didn't just miss promotion (clue 3), so Carl's team is Ludford Town. Willie's surname isn't Flagg (clue 5), so Grayburn Athletic was promoted. By elimination, Swanfield United just avoided relegation and Flagg's side is Padbury Rovers. Flagg isn't Tim (clue 3), so Bernie and Tim is the Midchester City fan. Tim is thus Barrier (clue 1) and Willie is Pitch.

In summary:
Bernie Flagg, Padbury Rovers, mid-table.
Carl Stand, Ludford Town, just missed promotion.
Simon Turnstyle, Swanfield United, just avoided relegation.
Tim Barrier, Midchester City, relegated.
Willie Pitch, Grayburn Athletic, promoted.

Puzzle No 92 On Site

The man aged 22 isn't Lance or Bob (clue 1), Darren (clue 2), or Robin (clue 6), so Sean. Lance and Bob are in their thirties (clue 1), as is Robin (clue 6), so Darren is 28. Thus

Solutions

Sean whistles (clue 2). Lance has long, dark hair and Bob tells jokes (clue 1). The man with the shaven head who asks silly questions isn't 28 (clue 3), so he's Robin. The man aged 33 with fair hair (clue 5) is Bob. Sean hasn't red hair (clue 4), so short, dark hair and Darren's is red. Robin isn't 37 (clue 6), so 31 and Lance is 37. Darren talks football (clue 6) and Lance sings.

In summary:
Bob, 33, fair hair, tells jokes.
Darren, 28, red hair, talks football.
Lance, 37, long, dark hair, sings.
Robin, 31, shaven head, asks silly questions.
Sean, 22, short, dark hair, whistles.

Puzzle No 93 Order Papers
The newsagent in Carlton Street ordered 40 copies of the Evening News (line 2) and the shop that ordered 50 Evening Mails also ordered 30 of the News (line 7), so the Gladstone Square shop, which ordered 60 Mails (line 5) but not 10 or 20 copies of the News (line 6) ordered 50 of the News. Silverman ordered 30 of the News (line 6) and thus 50 Mails (line 7). Pargetter took 30 Mails (line 3). Clark's is on the railway station (line 1). Since Lacey's didn't order 50 copies of the News (line 10), the Gladstone Square shop is Melville's. Clark didn't order 40 Mails (line 1), so 20. Clark didn't order 20 copies of the News (line 9), so 10. Silverman's shop isn't in Abbey Mews (lines 7 and 8), so Maidenwell and the Abbey Mews newsagent ordered 20 copies of the News. Pargetter's is in Carlton Street (lines 3 and 4) and the Abbey Mews shop ordered 40 Mails and is Lacey's.

In summary:
Clark, railway station, 20 Mails and 10 News.
Lacey, Abbey Mews, 40 Mails and 20 News.
Melville, Gladstone Square, 60 Mails and 50 News.
Pargetter, Carlton Street, 30 Mails and 40 News.
Silverman, Maidenwell, 50 Mails and 30 News.

Puzzle No 94 Things That Go Bump...
The 14th-century apparition haunting location is outside the manor (clue 3), but isn't the rooftop (clue 4), so the terrace. The apparition which shrieks belongs to the 15th century (clue 5). The screams come from the rooftop (clue 3). The poltergeist is silent and belongs to the 18th century (clue 1). The noise made by the 14th-century apparition isn't screams or groans (clue 3), so whistles. The 14th-century apparition isn't the ghost (clue 2) or kelpie (clue 4), so the banshee. The apparition in the hall is from the 15th century (clue 3). The poltergeist doesn't haunt the main bedroom (clue 1), so the drawing room and the groaning spook haunts the main bedroom. The male ghost doesn't shriek (clue 4), so groans. The kelpie screams (clue 2) and the female ghost shrieks. The kelpie is from the 16th century (clue 4) and the poltergeist from the 18th, so the male ghost is from the 17th century.

In summary:
Banshee, whistles, terrace, 14th century.
Female ghost, shrieks, hall, 15th century.
Kelpie, screams, rooftop, 16th century.
Male ghost, groans, main bedroom, 17th century.
Poltergeist, silence, drawing room, 18th century.

Puzzle No 95 Stagecoach

Chris Parker	John Blake
Simon Janssen	Hank Gudgeon
Victor Hennessey	Jake Verney

Les Stone	George Rackham
Roger Trent	Tom Luce
Colin Halliday	Pete Craski

Puzzle No 96 Seek and Ye Shall Find
The nail was found in strip A (clue 2) and Roy in strip E didn't find a coin (clue 6), so Stella's bottle top wasn't in strip F. The bottle top wasn't in D (clue 1) or B (clue 8), so C and (clue 1) Digger found the Roman coin in D. Roy didn't find the sixpence (clue 6), so he unearthed the washer (clue 4) and the sixpence was found in F. By elimination, the ring was in B, so (clue 3) Tanya Hunt was in A. The man surnamed Quest wasn't in E or F (clue 4), so B. Roy's surname is Search and Bleep was in F (clue 5), so Stella's surname is Seeking. Josie wasn't in D (clue 6), so F. Michael was in B (clue 7) and Eddie in D.

In summary:
A, Tanya Hunt, nail.
B, Michael Quest, ring.
C, Stella Seeking, bottle top.
D, Eddie Digger, Roman coin.
E, Roy Search, washer.
F, Josie Bleep, sixpence.

Puzzle No 97 Pandemonium Properties
The two pairs of ages referred to in clue 6 are 22/40 and 34/28, so the joiner wasn't 32. Those aged 22 and 28 weren't the bookkeeper (clue 1), security guard (clue 2) or wheelwright (clue 5), so painter and/or joiner. Thus Rotundus was either 34 or 40 (clue 6). Radius wasn't the painter (clue 3) or joiner (clue 6), so was also 34 or 40. The tenant of No 4 wasn't 28 (clue 2), so 22; thus Radius was 40 and Rotundus was 34 and was the security guard. Radius wasn't at No 3 or No 5 (clue 3) or No 1 (clue 4), so No 2. The 32-year-old was thus at No 3 (clue 4), the 28-year-old at No 1 and Rotundus at No 5. The tenant of No 1 wasn't Dexterus (clue 1) or Industrius (clue 2), so Nitidus. Radius was the wheelwright (clue 5). Industrius was the bookkeeper (clue 2), who thus lived at No 3 and Dexterus was the painter at No 4.

Solutions

In summary:
No 1, Nitidus, 28, joiner.
No 2, Radius, 40, wheelwright.
No 3, Industrius, 32, bookkeeper.
No 4, Dexterus, 22, painter.
No 5, Rotundus, 34, security guard.

Puzzle No 98 On the Oche
The English player's wife is Gloria (clue 4) and the American's surname is Flight (clue 6). Ruth's boyfriend Double, isn't Willie the Scotsman (clue 1), so Double is the Welshman. He isn't Tony aged 33 (clues 1 and 7), or Cliff (clue 8), so Nick. Nick isn't 27 (clue 4) and Gail's husband is 31 (clue 5), so he's 29 and scored 12 maximums (clue 2) and (clue 4) Board is 27. The English player scored 13 maximums (clue 4), so (clue 6) Flight registered 11 and was thus cheered on by Jenny (clue 3). By elimination, Willie had 10 maximums and his supporter is Gail, Board is English thus he's Cliff, Tony is American and Willie's surname is Bull.

In summary:
Cliff Board, England, 27, 13 maximums, Gloria.
Nick Double, Wales, 29, 12 maximums, Ruth.
Tony Flight, USA, 33, 11 maximums, Jenny.
Willie Bull, Scotland, 31, 10 maximums, Gail.

Puzzle No 99 Guardians of the Gates
Lurgan is at gate 2 (clue 2) and the guard at 4 has an axe (clue 4). Glun with poison darts isn't at gate 1 (clue 3), so 3. Zabec isn't at gate 4 (clue 4), so 1 and Tribb is at 4. The Quarg guard with the laser gun (clue 1) is Zabec and Lurgan has grenades. The guard from Blunk is at gate 2 (clue 3), so the one from Nuglon is at gate 4 (clue 2) and Glun is from Dozar.

In summary:
Gate 1, Zabec, Quarg, laser gun.
Gate 2, Lurgan, Blunk, grenades.
Gate 3, Glun, Dozar, poison darts.
Gate 4, Tribb, Nuglon, axe.

Puzzle No 100 Military Mutts
Arrow and Demon have the two handlers with six-letter surnames (clue 3), so since Scout's handler isn't Sergeant Whippet (clue 5), he's Lance-Corporal Griffon, posted to Colchester (clue 1) and Sergeant Whippet's dog is Kerry, who is cream (clue 2). The man going to Edinburgh is Corporal Talbot (clue 5) whose dog is black and tan (clue 4). Demon's handler is being posted to Hereford (clue 3), so (clue 3) he's Private Basset and Corporal Talbot's dog is Arrow. By elimination, Sergeant Whippet is going to Aldershot. Demon isn't black (clue 4), so grey and Scout is black.

In summary:
Private Basset, Demon, grey, Hereford.
Lance-Corporal Griffon, Scout, black, Colchester.
Corporal Talbot, Arrow, black and tan, Edinburgh.
Sergeant Whippet, Kerry, cream, Aldershot.

Puzzle No 101 Faraway Places
Dr Cheviot was the companion in July 1884 (clue 5). The expedition with Prof Mendip discovered the gorge and wasn't that in March 1882 which went to West Africa (clue 3). The March 1887 companion was Major Malvern or Colonel Lennox (clue 2), so Prof Mendip went on the January 1889 expedition. The South American expedition which found the waterfall was in March 1887 (clue 1) and the mountain was found in July 1884. By elimination, the lake was found in March 1882. The companion on that trip wasn't Major Malvern (clue 3), so Colonel Lennox and Major Malvern went to South America. The Australian expedition wasn't in January 1889 (clue 4), so July 1884 and the one to Central Africa was in January 1889.

In summary:
March 1882, West Africa, Colonel Lennox, lake.
July 1884, Australia, Dr Cheviot, mountain.
March 1887, South America, Major Malvern, waterfall.
January 1889, Central Africa, Professor Mendip, gorge.

Puzzle No 102 Lookalikes
Kate's surname is Clark (clue 4). The traffic warden's isn't Baker thus Ms Dixon isn't Iris (clue 2) or Lucy (clue 5), so Jane who looks like Dolly Parton (clue 3). The waitress is like Jane Fonda (clue 5). Ms Adams isn't like Maureen Lipman (clue 2), so Marilyn Monroe. Ms Adams isn't a housewife (clue 1), traffic warden (clue 2) or waitress (clue 5), so a nurse. If she's Iris, then (clue 2) the Maureen Lipman lookalike would be Ms Baker, the traffic warden is Kate Clark and (by elimination) Ms Dixon is the waitress who looks like Jane Fonda; but (above) Jane Dixon looks like Dolly Parton, so Iris isn't the nurse. Thus Iris is Ms Baker, Kate resembles Maureen Lipman and Jane is the traffic warden. By elimination, Ms Adams is Lucy, Iris is the waitress and the housewife is Kate Clark.

In summary:
Iris Baker, waitress, Jane Fonda.
Jane Dixon, traffic warden, Dolly Parton.
Kate Clark, housewife, Maureen Lipman.
Lucy Adams, nurse, Marilyn Monroe.

Puzzle No 103 Ghost Storeys
Brother Luke appears in tower A (clue 4). The New Tower is haunted by Lady Edith (clue 2), so (clue 2) the Sorcerer's Den isn't A or B. The room in C is the King's Chamber (clue 1), so the Sorcerer's Tower is D and (clue 2), the New Tower is C and Lady Edith haunts the King's Chamber. The room in B isn't the Treasure Room (clue 4), so the Whistling Room. B isn't Drogo's Tower (clue 3), so the Black Tower. By elimination, A is Drogo's Tower and has the Treasure Room. The tower B ghost isn't Lord Ivo (clue 4), so Old Meg and Lord Ivo haunts D.

In summary:
A, Drogo's Tower, Treasure Room, Brother Luke.
B, Black Tower, Whistling Room, Old Meg.
C, New Tower, King's Chamber, Lady Edith.
D, Sorcerer's Tower, Sorcerer's Den, Lord Ivo.